Mississippi Calling

MISSISSIPPI CALLING

BOOKS BY VIRGINIA S. EIFERT

THREE RIVERS SOUTH
A Story of Young Abe Lincoln

THE BUFFALO TRACE
The Story of Abraham Lincoln's Ancestors

OUT OF THE WILDERNESS
Young Abe Lincoln Grows Up

MISSISSIPPI CALLING

MISSISSIPPI CALLING

BY

VIRGINIA S. EIFERT

Illustrated by Manning de V. Lee

DODD, MEAD & COMPANY · New York · 1957

ACKNOWLEDGMENTS
AND DEDICATION

Mississippi Calling is dedicated with my grateful thanks to all those people and boats who contributed in various ways to my obtaining the material for this book, as well as for that great quantity of additional adventures, ideas and facts from which still other books will spring.

I am especially pleased to acknowledge the inspiration, assistance, transportation, information and other aid which were given freely and generously by Hazel and Gilbert Princell, through whose labors in my behalf I was first permitted to ride the river.

My deep thanks go to Elizabeth Golterman, Ruth Ferris, James V. Swift of *Waterways Journal*, and Marshall T. Gray of the U. S. Corps of Engineers, all of St. Louis; to Captain Frederick C. Way, Jr., of Sewickley, Pennsylvania; Marie C. Lala of New Orleans, Louisiana; Emma and Sidney Fell of Clearwater

v

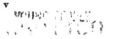

Lake, Wisconsin; Charlotte Du Bois of Minneapolis, Minnesota; Dr. and Mrs. Percival Robertson, Principia College, Elsah, Illinois; Dr. Thorne Deuel, Melvin L. Fowler and Dr. Wayne C. Temple of the Illinois State Museum, Springfield; to the librarians of Lincoln Library, and to Mrs. N. E. Nilsson, Mrs. C. R. Booth, Herman D. Eifert and Laurence N. Eifert, all of Springfield; also to *Nature Magazine*, issued by the Methodist Publishing Company.

My especial thanks go to George C. Keller and Edward Vorman and to Cities Service Refinery, Lake Charles, Louisiana, for their kindness and generosity in aiding my search for information.

Most particularly, this book must be dedicated to J. D. Streett and Company of St. Louis, and to R. H. Huffman, Kenneth Baker, and the late Harper C. Patton, officials of that company, who graciously permitted me to ride as a guest on their towboats for many thousands of miles on the Mississippi and its tributaries. To these boats, the *St. Louis Zephyr* and the *Cape Zephyr* —for boats are much like people, with personalities of their own —I say "thanks for the ride." My gratitude also goes to members of their crews, particularly to Captains W. M. Stiles and Hugh Leonard, and to Herman Merritt, engineer, of the *St. Louis Zephyr*, and to Captains Rolland W. Griffin, S. J. Joseph, Leonard Houchin and Homer Brazie; to engineers Marion Stoelting and William Johnson; and to R. W. Milam, William Vickers, Samuel Glasscock, Ilar Wilson, Howard Terlin, Max Fridell and Mr. and Mrs. Chester Todd, all of the *Cape Zephyr*, for extra courtesies and willing assistance at all times.

Mississippi Calling, therefore, belongs to all these people as their particular property. Yet, in a larger sense, perhaps it should also be dedicated to the big river itself, to the Mississippi, forever calling.

Virginia S. Eifert
Springfield, Illinois

The general situation and most of the events described in this book are based upon historical facts. However, certain fictional characters are wholly imaginative: they do not portray and are not intended to portray any actual persons.

MISSISSIPPI CALLING

CHAPTER ONE

9,000 B.C. ". . . . *a store
of glacial meltings filled the vale . . ."*
MASTERS

FIVE brown men crouched at the foot of an overhanging sand-stone cliff and watched the water. Over night, while they had slept by a fire which had warmed the rock with reflected heat and kept them comfortable through the chill spring darkness, the great river had quietly risen until it lay turbidly surging among the willows and lapping around the base of the rock shelter. Their protection had become a prison.

There was nothing the five could do: nothing but watch. They and their people had often camped here but never had they seen the Mississippi come so close. One man nudged his nearest fellow and pointed. His companion looked and grunted, and the

eyes of the others followed where the two stared. They saw that
the river swirled into all the hollows of rock so that their camping place was surrounded on three sides by water, with the overhanging cliff at their backs. The submerged shore was too steep,
they felt, the river too deep to attempt to wade it to safety. It
was too far to flounder to a place where they could hope to
climb up. The five were terrified of swimming the mighty river
at any time. Knowing the character of that stream, however,
they felt that the rise was but a temporary one. In a little while,
in a few hours, the big water would slide back again, and they
could escape. But the hours went by, and still the water came
closer.

The brown hunters crouching in the rock shelter along the
Mississippi in southern Illinois, eleven thousand years ago,
could not know that, only four hundred-odd miles to the north
of them, the dirty, crumbling wall of the last great glacier was
melting more rapidly than before, with the coming of warm
spring winds from the south. For thousands of years it had been
lessening, had been growing smaller and had been filling the
Mississippi and its valley with melt-water. Its drainage swelled
the river in a tremendous channel, while sudden rises sent it
surging along the bases of the cliffs.

The story of the great river and its valley went back much
farther in time than that remote period of the earliest men who
knew its muddy shores and hurrying waters. The story tells of
how, ages earlier, the seas came into the middle of North America and lay deeply over a countryside now long since forgotten
by marine waters. While the warm seas covered much of the
Mississippi Valley, its inhabitants—corals and crinoids, snails and
clams, brachiopods and trilobites—multiplied by millions and
died by millions. Calcium carbonate from their bodies sank to
the bottom and stacked up as a slowly hardening, limey sediment. When the seas went away, there lay great beds of limestone, hundreds of feet thick, in which were embedded the fossils

and imprints of animals whose myriad lives built the rock itself. In other places, sandy sediment became sandstone. One day those rocks would be chiseled out by moving river water to stand as cliffs along the Mississippi.

For millions of years there must have been a river running down what is now the Mississippi Valley. It may have been there two hundred and fifty million years ago. The seas had retreated and in their place lay warm Carboniferous swamps, tall with great fern trees and giant club mosses as big as oaks, whose decaying trunks and leaves in the muck eventually changed to coal.

And when the coal forests also vanished and time went on and on, there came at last a lovely era when the first flowering trees replaced the fern swamps, when the first willows, magnolias, poplars and sycamores grew along the great river.

The river and its valley had known many changes, but one of the most momentous came with the Glacial Era, a million years ago. Long before the early men arrived, ice out of Hudson Bay extended far down the Mississippi. The latter was shoved about, sent down the Illinois River Valley; ice bandied the Missouri and the Ohio until they and the Mississippi came to flow where they do today.

While the glacier lay a mile thick over the upper Mississippi Valley, blotting out all its wildlife, the climate was cool and moist below the ice. In great marshes watered by the melting glacier, the giant beaver sat on its furry haunches and, with a great noise of chomping, methodically cut down poplars and willows to build dams across streams flowing into the Mississippi. Herds of tempery little musk-oxen trotted over the stony tundra below the wall of ice, or wheeled in a semi-circle to face down a huge bear or pack of wolves. There were enormous mastodons in the forests. Woolly mammoths ranged the open country or fed knee-deep in marshes along the Mississippi. Sometimes a mammoth fell to its death when the banks gave way under the great flood of glacier water draining down the river to meet the sea.

Although early men may have known the glacial floods and those great beasts, may have seen the ice itself looming to the north, they did not know what was happening to their valley. For ever since the river had begun to flow, it had picked up in its gnawing waters billions of tons of earth grains which were dropped when the river reached sea level. So great had been the load and so broad its distribution as the river entered the Gulf, just below the tip of Illinois, that finally new land began to emerge from the sea. It was a muddy shore, bare and soft where the sea birds fed, but as the river continued to dump more and more earth, it shoved the land farther and farther southward. As the delta land built up, the Gulf of Mexico receded until it came to its present shores. But the delta did not stop. It has shoved a tongue of land more than a mile out into the Gulf of Mexico, the river flowing upon its elevation, and it continues to build land at the rate of 260 feet a year.

The river had built part of a continent, had laid down the kingdom of the Archaic Hunters and the Hopewellians, created the hunting grounds of the Taensas and the Natchez, built up the homeland of the Choctaws and Chickasaws. From its brief early route to a nearby Gulf of Mexico, the Mississippi world of the early men had become divided into three separate sections which even today are much unlike each other. They hardly seem to belong to the same huge and complicated stream with a length of 2,552 miles.

From the source of the river to that point called St. Anthony's Falls, at Minneapolis–St. Paul, the shallow Mississippi wanders on top of its valley. Between the Falls and the mouth of the Ohio, it has carved a route through rocky cliffs, so that the river now lies well below water-chiseled hills and bluffs—a walled river. From the Ohio to the Gulf of Mexico, the Mississippi is a built-up river, traveling on its own mud-layered bed, as if on a trough which frequently lies higher than the land sloping down on either side.

This, then, was the river of the early men, homeland of those five crouching at the mercy of the Mississippi, with the cliff at their backs, the water before them, and all hope lost.

They might not have found themselves in this situation if the Ice Age had not, long ago, guided their ancestors to the North American continent. The Ice Age froze so much of the world's water that sea levels everywhere were greatly lowered. Thus a land bridge appeared which extended from Siberia to Alaska. A ridge of mountains marking the Aleutian Islands today is all that remains of that bridge. Over this natural causeway it is believed that America's first human inhabitants may have crossed Bering Straits. They followed the great beasts of the fantastic Pleistocene menagerie, hunted mammoths and camels and horses in Alaska. Then they evidently followed an unglaciated trough, a warmer passageway, southeast to a kinder climate.

Until that exciting day in 1925 when the bones of a ten-thousand-year-old Ice Age bison were discovered with a man-made flint spear embedded nearby, no one knew how far back human beings had lived in America. There had been no proof that they had ever hunted in this country during Pleistocene times, even though they were known to have done so in Europe. Now here was the proof.

Archaeologists called him Folsom Man, because his uniquely shaped spears were first found near Folsom, New Mexico, and they sought his remains across the arid lands of the West. But no early man of such an ancient birthday was located along the Mississippi nor east of the great river. This did not mean that he had not been there; it only indicated that his presence was hidden, lost in the enveloping mists of the past.

The five marooned hunters watched the water lapping closer. They were hungry; they were cold. This was the second day of their imprisonment, and their supply of firewood was meager. It was being kept in reserve as much as possible, only feeding the precious blaze to keep it alive for a little warmth, a little assurance. One man had caught a turtle which climbed out on the sand at his feet. Its stringy meat, heated over the small fire, fed the five but scantily. Several chipmunks crept to the dryness of the shelter and became food for the besieged hunters. A coot which waddled ashore was caught and eaten. And the water came a little closer and a little closer.

These five men would leave little evidence of their presence if the river claimed them; might leave little enough, even if they should escape. There would be no written record of a wandering prehistoric people, no pictured rocks; only their discarded or lost flints, the bones left from their meals and from their own deaths . . . these, and the mute charcoal of their many campfires. And for thousands of years these small records lay totally unknown beneath a certain rock shelter in southern Illinois.

It was always a favorite camping place. Early people along the Mississippi evidently used this rock shelter again and again. It was used for at least ten thousand years, extending from the final period of the Wisconsin Glacier until the time the Norsemen discovered America. After every campfire was burnt out, the blackened charcoal remained. The bones of meals which the hunters ate were scattered close by . . . bones of catfish, gar and drum, of turtle, teal and swan, of passenger pigeon, curlew and eagle. Bones of whitetail deer were extremely abundant, for deer were a common food, but there were no bison bones at all. This could mean that there were no bison east of the Mississippi in those days, or simply that the early hunters had not the weapons with which to kill such powerful game. Among the remains were bones of chipmunk, rabbit and raccoon, squirrel, skunk, fox and beaver. There were snail and clam shells, always a great quantity of clams taken from the shallows of the muddy river and the meat used as food.

The mysterious people left behind them some of their flints—

spears, axes, scrapers, drills, abraders, hammerstones—which were forgotten, lost or discarded. They left awls made of leg-bones of ducks and other large birds, drills made of deer ulnas, and sometimes an ornament fashioned of a clam shell whose interior had been used for food. Now and again a hunter died—perhaps from an encounter with a cougar, or from a fall from the cliff, or from some wasting disease—and his remains were casually left behind when the other hunters moved on.

It all came to that spot a little at a time, a piece here, a piece there, a spearpoint lost one week, an awl forgotten five years later, a dead hunter gone to his eternal rest some other time. Year after year, a small, fine rain of crumbling sandstone and earth from the top of the overhanging cliff sifted down into the shelter and gradually covered the earliest remains of campfires, flints and bones, then continued to cover later leavings as it continues to do today. Time went on for a long, long while and still the shelter was used by men along the Mississippi.

In the past eleven thousand years, some twenty-six feet or more of debris has covered the layered remains in this camp spot of Early Archaic hunters along the Mississippi. No one suspected that anything at all lay under the cliffs until road builders removed earth from the base of the cliffs, to use as a fill in the new highway between the old French town of Prairie du Rocher and the village of Modoc. At both ends of the area they left pillars of earth which stood nearly at the original height of the accumulation of deposits in the rock shelter. A few Indian artifacts and bones were picked up by casual bystanders. Not until an archaeological expedition, sponsored by the Illinois State Museum and the University of Chicago, investigated the site, years later, in 1952, did anyone suspect how ancient it was.

Excavation at first was begun in the pillars of earth left by the road builders. Here were countless layers of ash, charcoal and other evidences of ancient human occupation. A pit was taken down to many feet below the present ground level, with more exciting discoveries coming to light along the way.

Twenty-six feet down lay the charcoal and bones left by a people who had camped there while the last glacier still lurked four hundred miles away, in Minnesota and Wisconsin, when the Mississippi River was broader, muddier and more full of water than it has likely been since that time. But the excavators did not know how ancient their finds really were.

Without a certain discovery, the secrets of the rock shelter and its long-gone people might have been an unsolved riddle. It was the charcoal of old campfires which told the tale, for charcoal is burned wood, and wood was once alive. All living things contain radioactive isotopes, called Carbon 14, which are constantly being produced in the earth's atmosphere by the collision of cosmic rays with nitrogen atoms. The proportion of the radioactive isotopes, which is constant, is absorbed by living objects until their death. When life ends, Carbon 14 begins to disintegrate. After 5,568 years, about one half of this carbon is gone. And here lies the great secret, long hidden from mankind. By finding out the amount of radioactive carbon remaining in long-dead, once-living matter, the time of its death can be figured, thus dating it more accurately than was ever possible before.

Fragments of charcoal from the ancient fires of the hunters who had crouched in the rock shelter were tested at the University of Chicago laboratories, under the supervision of Dr. Willard Libby. And there it was: suddenly it was known how long ago, approximately, certain men sat around a campfire and gnawed bones of a roasted deer or goose or opossum. From the magical discoveries of the carbon test, it was decided that those campfires were burning six thousand to eleven thousand years ago, on the southern Illinois shore of the Mississippi River, a few miles downstream from St. Louis. It was longer ago—much, much longer—than anyone had ever dreamed that men had lived in the Mississippi Valley. The possibility grew, besides, that these men of the Modoc Rock Shelter might even have been there before Folsom Man left his beautiful spears among the bones of Taylor's bison, in prehistoric New Mexico.

Now to return to those five hunters marooned in the shelter. It was on the third day, perhaps, when their fire was all gone and the men had slept but poorly, because of the hunger gnawing at their very vitals, that they woke in the dim light of dawn and discovered a narrow strip of mud where there had been only Mississippi River water the day before. By the end of the day, the strip had widened enough so that the men, holding as best they could to the rough sandstone, could creep along to the spot where a trail would lead them to the heights. With renewed vigor, they trotted up the hill pathway, where spring blossoms welcomed them and birds sang in an April chorus.

It was some eleven thousand years later that bone fragments of turtle, coot and chipmunk—food which had sustained the early men cornered by the Mississippi—were carefully collected by other men intent upon learning all that was possible to be gleaned from the remains of people, animals and plants at that fascinating spot. Four miles away now, the Mississippi flowed toward the sea, as it has been flowing for more millennia than there have been men to see it. Long since, it has deserted much of its vast floodplain, which often was filled to the bases of the cliffs. But the Mississippi is an eternally changeable stream. One day it may again lap around the ancient sandstone of that rock shelter which for ten thousand years was a haven for prehistoric hunters in the great valley.

*

CHAPTER TWO

1200 A D. ". . . *abandoned to those gravitations*
    Which crumble pyramids, and change the nations."
                                            MASTERS

W E shall build to the Lord Sun a temple greater than any
he has ever seen!" boasted the High Priest. "A temple which
will receive many sacrifices. It must be higher above the ground,
higher above the common people, and hence nearer the sun,
than ever a temple has been built before!"

The rich Mississippi men, dressed in woven robes and decorated with ropes of river pearls and carved clamshell amulets
hung around their necks, looked doubtfully about them. They
knew how long it took the women and slaves to build even an
ordinary mound as a burial place for a wealthy man and his
family. To erect a mound such as the High Priest demanded,

10

which he was insisting upon so insolently, would take years. Only the Sun God himself knew how many women and slaves would wear out their lives heaping up the earth to his glory. Besides, there was neither hill nor hummock to build it upon, for the floodplain of the Mississippi had been leveled by many a high water. The nearest hills lay miles to the east, or across the Mississippi to the west.

"The greatest temple mound ever built!" repeated the High Priest implacably, and the rich men backed away, bowing low, murmuring agreement.

And so the women and the captive slaves went to work. They had no choice in the matter. Only the wives of rich men did not have to labor, but had many slaves to do their bidding It was the wives and daughters of the common people living in the thousands of little grass and log houses in the lowland who labored. Men were hunters, traders, farmers, not common burden bearers.

Day after day, as the summer sun bore down upon the steaming, humid, Mississippi bottomland, the women patiently scraped up the baked black earth with their clamshell scoops and filled their woven reed baskets. And they carried their loads to the little heap which was all that showed, after weeks of work, where the Great Mound one day would rise.

Nearly ten thousand years had passed since five hunters had crouched in a rock shelter in southern Illinois, a few miles from where the Great Mound rose. A long, long time before the great structure was begun, people who followed the Early Archaic hunters dwelt in the pleasant world of the Mississippi Valley. Today they are called Hopewellians, but no one knows what they may have called themselves, for no written word was left behind to reveal the ways and secrets of these early people. Yet theirs became one of the most highly developed civilizations in prehistoric North America. Although these forerunners of the modern American Indian lived from western New York State to Kansas, the Hopewellians were largely inhabitants of the Great Valley. Their biggest towns were centered on the Ohio, the Illinois, and down along the broad floodplain of the Mississippi.

They were people of the river. They lived along its shores and found much of their food in the water itself, in the swamps and marshes, in the forests and uplands. Besides, unlike the Early Archaic people, the Hopewellians were not wandering hunters, but farmers and traders. Long ago they had learned how to plant seeds and how to raise crops for food, so that it was no longer necessary to range over hundreds of miles along the Mississippi and the prairie to find food enough to sustain a single family.

In this lower valley where the long growing season and lengthy days of sunshine were perfect for maturing crops, the increasing populations of copper-skinned people learned to cultivate their beans and squash and their fields of maize so that the yield was increased, yet the work was less. Because of this, they found more time for leisure—and leisure was something new in man's usual hand-to-mouth existence. It meant that life could contain something more than hunting, fishing, farming, harvesting, eating and sleeping, with occasional wars and occasional moves to a new village site when food ran short or debris stacked too high around the old one.

It may have been because of this new leisure that the more intelligent Hopewellians began to develop a way of life which was rising above that of the common man; and this, too, was something new. One of the by-products of leisure was business. The Hopewellians were traders, early businessmen along the Mississippi. They pushed extensive trading operations throughout much of the country. They paddled big dugout canoes loaded with trade goods and came back at last, after long and hazardous journeys, with grizzly-bear teeth from the Rocky Mountains, large marine shells from the South Atlantic coast and the Gulf of Mexico, sheet mica from North Carolina, copper from the Lake Superior country. The Hopewellians paddled far up the Mississippi, the Missouri, the Ohio, the Kentucky, the

Arkansas, the Cumberland, the Tennessee and lesser rivers, long before any white men knew that the continent of North America existed. Some of the Hopewellians became very rich from their trading. They and their wives, therefore, dressed more elaborately than the farmers and wore more costly ornaments of copper, bears' teeth, mica, and ropes of big, softly shining pearls from river clams. When these people died, their insignia of rank and some of their wealth were buried with them in special mounds which were built tall above the level floor of the flood plain, or set upon bluffs and hills. The size of a man's burial mound, finally, became a sign of his degree of importance in the community.

Another outgrowth of leisure was religion. Because the Hopewellians were a people who depended upon the sun to make their most vital food—maize—grow and ripen, they worshipped the sun. Eventually, in order to properly pay homage to the Lord Sun, there were priests who invented strange rituals and who ordered temples built on certain mounds erected for the purpose. Around the temples, cities grew where small, transient villages had been before.

After centuries of Hopewellian domination along the Mississippi and the Ohio, trouble began to brew down the Valley. The Hopewellian paradise was suddenly threatened. It happened that southward along the great river there dwelt other people, the Middle Mississippians, who for some time had looked not only with awe but with considerable jealousy at the prosperous Hopewellians and their ceremonies and mounds, at their temples and at their undeniable wealth.

One day, therefore, trouble erupted violently. A well planned attack on an undefended Hopewellian town caught the inhabitants desperately unprepared. The town was easily taken, and the blood-thirsty Middle Mississippians, overwhelming town after town, surged northward up the river. The Hopewellians had spent too much time with their trading, their elaborate religious rituals, and their easy life to be ready to defend themselves. And the great culture of the Hopewellians, bathed in blood and flame, vanished.

The arrogant and triumphant Middle Mississippians took over the towns or built new ones. Since they had evidently envied and admired the Hopewellians, they probably patterned their customs on those which they had watched so jealously from afar. They, too, built mounds, but larger mounds. They developed ceremonies which were even more elaborate than Hopewellian rites. The Middle Mississippian towns were greater, the conquerors boasted, than any decadent Hopewellian city ever built along the river.

The climax came in the area now encompassed, in part, by Cahokia Mounds State Park, in Illinois, across from St. Louis. This area occupied the rich bottomland where the Mississippi floodplain fans out in fertile black earth as level as a floor and extended across the river to the hills on which St. Louis later was built. What was probably the biggest city of prehistoric people in North America rose in that bottomland. There were thousands of houses made of wood and cane, thatched with grass. The homes of the rich men and priests were elevated on mounds. Cultivated fields lay in the distance, and great numbers of people dwelt under the rule of priests and chiefs.

And then it was that the High Priest ordered the greatest mound of all to be built as a temple to the sun.

The women and slaves worked until winter came and bound the river bottom earth with deep-set frost, so that the clamshell scoops broke when they tried to scrape it up. But winter lasted only a short time in the lower Mississippi Valley, and even in Illinois, where the Middle Mississippi people had their greatest city, the frost often went out of the ground in late January and it was seldom frozen for long after that.

The women and slaves labored for months, for years. Thousands of baskets were worn out and dumped with their last load of earth onto the pile. Then another one would be taken for the next loads. Women too old to work on the mound spent their days making baskets. And the earth in the mound rose higher . . . higher . . . higher.

A long, long time after the High Priest demanded a mound, the great pyramid was finished. It was made level and smooth on top for the temple, while a second level, perhaps for priests' houses, lay a short distance below the summit. The structure was 1,080 feet long, 710 feet wide and 100 feet high, made of bottomland earth pounded hard and plastered with mud which dried almost like stone. A flight of steps set into the steep side of the mound ascended to the temple, which may have been decorated with turtle-shell shields and tribal banners, and with poles on which the buzzard-picked skulls of sacrificial victims were impaled. And so the High Priest, perhaps, was satisfied.

So a thousand years ago, the Mississippi People, with clam-shell scoops and the strength of many women and slaves, built a mountain on a plain. The Mississippi Pyramid is bigger in bulk than the Great Pyramid which was built several thousand years earlier along the Egyptian Nile. Today, it is one of the greatest primitive earthworks in the world.

When it was completed, around it lay three hundred lesser mounds, the burial places for the rich. With the temple mound as its hub, extending for eight miles in the flood plain, the great city flourished.

When Columbus discovered the New World, the Indian population of America, and especially in that fertile world along the great river, was very likely at its peak; but no white man saw the Hopewellians or the Mississippians. They were gone, their story vanished, when white explorers discovered the Mississippi. By that time, the Indians who lived there knew nothing of the people who had preceded them as inhabitants along the river. They were unaware of what sort of persons had built the mysterious mounds, nor did they understand why those builders had gone away. Yet many of the old customs lingered, as, for example, among the mound-building, sun-worshipping Natchez who lived down the river. If anyone had known it, these were a direct link with the past.

And the Mississippi, in its periods of flood, rose and filled the floodplain and licked around the bases of the mounds, but it could not wash them away—nor has it succeeded in doing so to this day The mounds which lay where St. Louis was built were sheared off, shoveled away. Many of those around the great pyramid mound met their end under the blades of plows digging fields for corn. The frail thatched houses of the early people vanished and so did the temples and ornaments which were part of the ceremonies honoring the Sun God.

Today, the Mississippi Pyramid, still surrounded by a few of the lesser mounds, has been preserved in a state park. It is half covered with trees, but the top where the temple stood is still level and smooth. It is a massive chunk of earth, a truncated pyramid, silhouetted against the sky. And the Sun God himself continues to burn above the steamy Mississippi Valley, where the maize fields of other peoples grow and flourish under his hot, beneficent rays.

CHAPTER THREE

1542: "O River of Yesterday, with current swift . . .
O River of Tomorrow . . .
I follow, follow where thy waters run."
LONGFELLOW

Hernando DE SOTO was dying His great strength exhausted, he lay on a rude bed made of skins and Indian shawls. There, inside the dusky bark hut which he had taken from the Chief of Guachoya, the dying Governor of Cuba and Adelantado of Florida knew that death was near. His great plans for discovering and conquering new lands, of amassing riches in gold and silver and precious stones in the New World, would never be carried out. This was the end. Almost half of the six hundred men who had started out with him from Cuba three years before had died, either from diseases which struck them down or from

Indians who did the same thing in a quicker but usually more dreadful manner. No Indian arrow had touched Hernando De Soto, but illness was going to end his life as finally and deliberately as a Chickasaw spearpoint in his heart.

Not far away from the hut where he lay there flowed the massive river, the River Grande, *Río Espiritu Santo*, River of the Holy Spirit, the dreadful, heartless Mississippi. This was the river which had caused him so much anguish and which promised now to destroy him and his plans.

It was May, 1542, and outside De Soto's primitive Arkansas hut a mockingbird splattered a bright and gusty melody into the warm sunshine. White egrets and blue herons waded in the wild swampland below the mouth of the Arkansas River. Early summer was already upon the South.

In a floating sort of languor, De Soto's mind drifted back over the things which had taken place in those three hideous, disappointing years. He let his mind wander lazily, without really caring, which alternate course might have proved better to follow than the one he had chosen. At the time, he had been so sure he was right in his decision. . . . He wondered whether it would have been better to have entered Florida with gifts and friendship for the Indians, rather than with bloodshed and violence, in the Spanish fashion . . . whether he should or should not have kidnapped the beautiful Queen of Cutifachiqui, as he had . . . whether her pearls were really so valuable. . . . Whether the lying youth knew what he was about, leading them all so terribly astray in search of a nation which possessed much gold, or if he was only mad, after all. Whether Doña Ysabel, De Soto's wife, still waited for him in Cuba, and if she would ever know his fate . . . if anyone would ever know . . . or learn of the fate of these last three hundred hapless men, lost with him in the great wilderness along the River Grande.

A red carp splashed in the muddy waters of the river which was dazzling with sun sparkle, waters pouring relentlessly, heedless of him or of any man, down to the sea . . . if he only knew how far away was the sea . . .

Hernando De Soto had helped Pizarro conquer Peru in 1531. He came highly recommended to the job of subduing Florida and its vast wastes in the name of Spain. Pizarro's method had been to kill, rob and destroy. It worked. De Soto would repeat the procedure in North America. Florida was the name given to all that new land lying north of Mexico, but no one knew how really vast it was, knew of its mountains, its rivers, its forests and deserts and plains. It was De Soto's job to find out, and to take its treasure—especially the treasure.

Seven ships rounded the Florida peninsula to the southwest and came up to what is now Charlotte Harbor, near Tampa. On May 30, 1539, six hundred men, 213 horses and a herd of Spanish hogs came ashore. At sight of them, the Indians abruptly departed from their village called Ucita, which contained eight houses made of timber and thatched with palm leaves. The Spaniards immediately took this over as a base camp. De Soto then sent the ships back to Cuba, with orders to return at an appointed time with supplies So on a June day the seven ships sailed off again into the hazy blue of the sea's horizon, with the gulls crying after them, while the conquerors stood on the shore and watched the lifeline binding them with civilization vanish, leaving an empty sea. White waves curled small on the white sand, and sea birds piped and cried above the encampment of six hundred suddenly lonely and deserted men.

Plainly, there was no gold in Ucita. Leaving some of the men at the base camp set in the sand and pines, the rest of the expedition—hogs, horses and men—started north. Very early in the journey, the Spaniards discovered they did not like Florida. They tramped, hungry and mosquito-bitten, in a low, wet, swampy country, thickly covered with cypresses and bristly palmettos. Food was scarce. The men were soldiers, not hunters; they did not, in fact, know anything about living off the country.

THE
UPPER
MISSISSIPPI

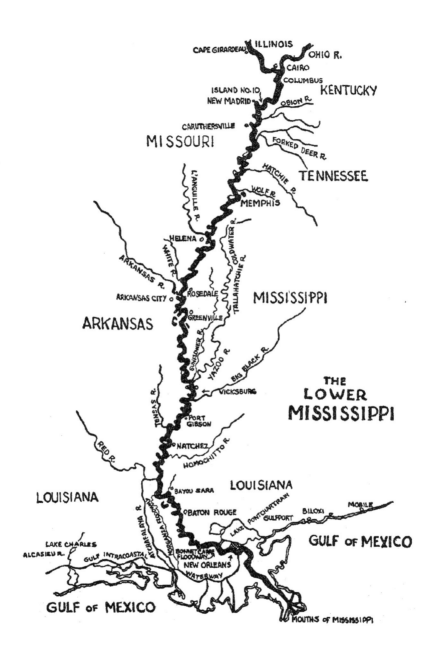

THE
LOWER
MISSISSIPPI

Theirs was a long, discouraging, blood-stained journey from Ucita northward and around the curve of the Gulf of Mexico to Apalachee Bay. Once there, the men were eager to go back.

Far from returning, De Soto sent for the men at the base camp to join them. And the army of ever hungry, unhappy, gold-hunting soldiers pushed forward. Led by a skinny Indian youth, babbling of gold in quantity in a town to the north, the expedition went on wearily into South Carolina. . . . They came at last to the town of Cutifachiqui, whose lovely young queen entertained and feasted them.

After many days of rest and enjoyment, coupled with good food, De Soto, in his abrupt way, ordered his army on the march again. They had dallied too long and the supply ships would have come and gone unless the expedition hurried. The men grumbled, but set off to the west, heading through the trackless wilderness of the Great Smoky Mountains.

De Soto, coveting the queen's pearls, had kidnapped his beautiful hostess and several of her women. Her dark eyes somber, the queen walked silently over the rough trails; one of her women carried the casket of pearls. But high in the Smokies, the Queen of Cutifachiqui escaped. She and her women slipped off into the laurels and were lost to pursuit. De Soto was chagrined. He did not mind so much that the captives had escaped, but it grieved him that he had lost the pearls.

The exploration party reached the Tennessee River above Chattanooga, turned southwest, crossed the Black Warrior River, came into Alabama.

There disaster struck. Indians at Mauilla attacked. Howling, leaping, tossing firebrands, they liberated the chained Indian slaves, who had been taken along to act as servants to the soldiers, and gave them bows and arrows with which to fight the white men. And, because these slaves had been carrying all the extra clothing, pearls and possessions of the Spaniards, they neatly robbed their captors of much that they owned. There was, besides, a dreadful toll of dead.

Desperately, De Soto managed to get his battered men and horses and most of his precious hogs out of Mauilla. The army pushed on into Mississippi, to the Chickasaw town of Chicaça, which they took over and where they stayed for the winter. It was much too late to get to the coast and meet the ships. It had been so much farther from the Smokies to the sea than De Soto had thought. He would not admit that he was lost in the American wilderness. Doubtless, the supply ships had come and, thinking him dead, their crews had sailed back to Cuba. Poor Doña Ysabel, De Soto pondered with a remote sort of grief, she will think herself a widow now, and well she may be, in fact.

March, 1541 . . . four o'clock in the morning. Everyone was asleep in the chill spring dampness before dawn when the Indians of Chicaça, revolting, attacked. They set fire to the houses, then waited at the gates to slaughter the Spaniards as they rushed out. Many horses died in the flames, and with them four hundred hogs and eleven Spaniards. Most of the men had left their clothing in their huts when the blaze started, and they were shivering dreadfully in the March cold. Some of them managed to make mats of dried grasses sewed together somehow, and wrapped them around themselves. A few of the haughty Castilians laughed, but they were the ones who had some clothing left. The others were thankful to have anything between them and the breeze, and laughter didn't hurt them.

The bedraggled, makeshift, unhappy, hungry, fearful soldiers made camp at an Indian town near a great river.

De Soto had almost forgotten the stories he had heard from De Vaca and others about the *Río Espiritu Santo*, the mysterious River of the Holy Spirit, which ran into the sea, from whence no one knew. The Indians now talked of a Great River, or called it simply *The River*, as if there were none other like it, as if it were truly a god. So De Soto went alone to look at this potent stream.

In his rusty armor and helmet, the tall, swarthy Spaniard, his tanned face lined, his eyes full of a growing despair which he fiercely would not admit even to himself, stood that spring day on the water-carved banks of the Mississippi River. The spot is believed to have been about thirty miles below the present town of Memphis, though the course of the river has changed so much since that day, no one can be certain as to the exact location.

A spring wind blew across his face. He took off his helmet and let the breeze blow through his black hair, and his brooding eyes watched how the river flowed, galloping in a great torrent, with trees and deadwood bounding along with it. The water was clouded by a great muddiness, and it churned under the embankment at his feet, so that he could see the earth being eaten away, bit by bit. The trees on the distant shore were so far off as to be blurred and indistinct. De Soto had never seen so large a river, had never dreamed of one so massive, so cruel, so implacable, so wide.

The Spaniard stood alone on the banks of the Mississippi. Suddenly, in the deepest humility and despair that he had ever known in all his arrogant, conquering career, Hernando De Soto dropped to his knees.

"Holy spirit, help me!" he cried aloud, lifting his clasped hands to the sky. And the river poured past him, unheeding.

After a long while, he got to his feet and went back to his harassed and weary people. De Anasco, De Guzman, and Luis De Moscoso were worried by his long absence, but they had not dared to go in search of him.

As if he had been given a message from the river itself, in answer to his dilemma, De Soto moved the entire camp to a level place near the Mississippi, as though in its very nearness he would find the solution to its crossing. Besides, there was a heavy stand of bottomland timber—sycamore, cottonwood, gum, pecan, tupelo, cypress—which would be excellent for use in building boats.

He ordered brought to the new camp and stored all the maize which he and his men had taken from villages in the rear. Then some set to work cutting down trees, while others sawed out planks to build barges. The men were equipped to do this, for wherever they had gone, carpenter tools had been carried by some of the foot soldiers or by the Indian slaves, and, providentially, these vital tools had not been lost in the fires at Chicaça and Mauilla.

The governor watched the activity. And from a distance, other eyes watched, too.

One day there was a great gathering of long dugouts on the river—two hundred canoes filled with Indians bearing weapons. The savages were painted with ochre to make themselves impressive. They carried shields decorated with the plumes of white herons and pink spoonbills, red ibis and green paroquets, and wore great bunches of egret plumes on their heads. Warriors in the long boats stood proudly and ceremoniously erect, holding bows and arrows and staring at the Spaniards, who stared back at them from the bank.

The chief of Aquixo came cautiously to shore and presented to De Soto a great quantity of freshly caught fish, together with some hard loaves the color of brick which were made of the pulp of dried persimmons.

The chief and De Soto exchanged polite compliments, warily. Then the visitor returned to his canoe and, as the two hundred other craft, with their awnings and plumes and shields and pennons, began to draw away from shore, the chief raised his hand in farewell. At that moment, some of De Soto's hotheaded crossbowmen, who couldn't restrain themselves, let fly with their arrows. Half a dozen Indians were struck down. The others paddled away rapidly in good order, while De Soto whirled on his men.

"You fools! You *fools!*" he roared. "You scatter your wits like peas to hens! There are times when a man must restrain his arrows, lest they fly back and destroy him. You saw the numbers of men in this fleet of canoes. They are only a portion of those dwelling on the other shore of the Great River. Would you inflame them, now, when we are in so desperate a strait?" And the governor stamped off to his house, then lay on his pallet, feeling a fever rise in his bones and his body burn.

On a morning in June, so early that there was no hint of light in the warm, dark sky and no birds but an owl and the chuckwills-widows were calling, the men of the camp were awake, ready to start the journey across the river. It was believed impossible to cross straight over. The current was too fast, the distance too great. But in his month beside the Mississippi, De Soto had been studying that current. Consequently, he sent the barges and canoes up the river half a mile, hugging slack water along the shore. These craft then headed slantwise into the current and let it carry them down and across to the other side.

On the east bank, De Soto strained his eyes to see, but the darkness was still too thick, the river too wide, its morning mists too tenuous, for his eyes to pierce the mystery: did the boats get across safely?

Before he thought it possible, the barges and canoes were back, empty, ready for another load. They had made it, and no Indians had appeared anywhere. Soon there came a lightening to the east, a reflective shine in the river, from which the mists seemed to thicken and boil up as from a kettle. The air was loud with the twittering of swallows. Cardinals, orioles, and mockingbirds tuned up in the dew-dripping trees.

Back and forth, letting the current carry them as much as possible, the barges transported three hundred men and the horses across to the other shore. On the last trip, they carried Hernando De Soto. The sun was two hours' high, the mists had vanished, the sky was blue and hot, and still no Indians had appeared.

Looking back from the west shore, De Soto could not even make out where the camp had been. Watching from there earlier, he had not been able to discern men on the west shore, it was so far off. Thick and brown, full of driftwood and puffs of brown foam like floating bread, the river poured onward, seeking the sea. Over it that day had passed the first white men to cross the Mississippi. What lay beyond, none of them knew.

Immediately, De Soto and his men put their minds back upon the bloody business of conquering. Half-heartedly, they hunted for gold, but food was more important, and almost as scarce.

During months of summer heat the men tramped west and north, through Arkansas, and then, as autumn waned, they felt winter closing down. They made camp for several months on the Arkansas River before heading back, in despair, to the Mississippi. No gold . . . no gold . . .

April, 1542, and they were back on the west bank of the *Río Espiritu Santo*, the Great River, desperate to know what to do next. It was then that they learned about a big and powerful town down the river, called Quigaltam, whose inhabitants fought all who came near.

De Soto listened moodily to this piece of depressing news. He was very ill and weakness often overcame him these days. He sank back now on his bed and closed his eyes in a growing despondency. Men and horses were dying; the horses had no iron shoes for this rough country. The men were clad in rags and Indian moccasins, and they were thin and ill from improper food during all those three long, terrible years. Now, if he could enlist the aid of the chief of this powerful town of Quigaltam, he might hope to get to the coast. So De Soto, going about it the wrong way, in his final effort at being a conqueror, sent an arrogant message down to the chief of Quigaltam. He stated that he,

De Soto, was the Son of the Sun, and the chief must therefore visit him and pay him tribute with fine gifts and aid.

The answer which came back from the insulted chief of Quigaltam was the final blow which sapped the strength of the dying De Soto.

"As to what you say of your being the Son of the Sun," was the chief's icy reply, "if you will cause him to dry up the great river, I will believe you. As to the rest, it is not my custom to visit anyone, but rather, all of whom I have ever heard have come to visit me, to serve and obey me, and pay me tribute, either voluntarily or by force. If you desire to see me, come where I am. If for peace, I will receive you with special good will; if for war, I will await you in my town; but neither for you, nor for any man, will I set back one foot!"

De Soto's eyes flashed fury, and he sat up. No man in all of Florida, in all of Europe or Peru, had dared to speak so to him, the conqueror! If he only had the physical strength he once possessed . . . if he just had enough men and horses and arms, he would destroy this arrogant chief of Quigaltam, would devastate his lands, kill or capture all his people, burn his town . . . De Soto lay back dizzily with a groan, for he knew that those days were past, all past.

By the next morning, De Soto knew that his time was short. He called for his captains and from them he chose Luis De Moscoso to be the new leader.

On the following day, May 21, 1542, on the west bank of the Mississippi River, in the Indian town of Guachoya, a little way below the mouth of the Arkansas River, Hernando De Soto, the conqueror, departed this life.

Luis De Moscoso, the new commander, was worried. If the Indians knew that De Soto was dead, they, thinking the Son of the Sun immortal, might come and attack the town and kill all the white men for lying about him. For three days, therefore,

Don Hernando De Soto's body lay in the Indian hut. Then, on the third night, Luis De Moscoso and some of his men carried off the tall, rigid body of their former leader and buried it in a hastily dug, shallow grave near the gate of the town.

The next day, however, the Indians discovered the loose earth. They looked about, poked at it with their feet, talked among themselves, gesturing, whispering. Luis De Moscoso knew he must do something to allay their suspicions, so he and his men went out that night and brought up the remains of De Soto, wrapped in his burial shawls. They filled the shawls with sand, as much as they would hold, to weight them. Then, in the darkness, the men paddled out in a canoe and let the body of De Soto gently slide into the silent, moving, dark depths of the Mississippi. It went in with scarcely a splash. The starshine on the waters was hardly blurred.

It was next day that the chief of Guachoya bluntly asked Luis De Moscoso:

"What has been done with my brother and lord, the governor?"

Luis De Moscoso gulped. Now it had come!

"The governor," he began warily, "has ascended into the skies, as he has done on so many other occasions, to confer with God Himself. However, since he felt that he might be detained there for some time, he has left me in charge of the camp and the men."

The chief nodded politely, but quite unbelievingly.

"But yes, sire," he said, bowing. "That is your way of telling me that my lord is dead."

"But no!" protested Luis De Moscoso desperately. "I tell you that the governor is not dead, but only gone into the heavens. He will be back with us again very soon!"

The chief bowed, smiling to himself, and went away.

After that, the danger seemed to have been passed by. Luis De Moscoso went through De Soto's few belongings and put up all his property for sale, including seven hundred pigs. The governor had jealously guarded his precious swine, hoping to keep them until there should be enough to feed his army. But the Indians had taken some; others had run off; many more had been lost in the fires at Mauilla and Chicaça. Now they were eagerly bought by the soldiers, who signed notes that when they returned to Spain they would pay thus and so. After that, everyone feasted on roast pork. To be able to eat crisp, brown, roasted meat made new men of them.

On June 5, 1542, the expedition left Guachoya and the Mississippi and turned south-southwest. It had been decided by vote of the members to seek the sea by way of Mexico, since no one knew where the river went. They tramped through the Arkansas wilderness and into Texas, into the stark immensity of Texas, to wander lost, misled, starving again, through arid wastes and cactus country. It was horribly hot and dry. By early October, they knew that, if winter caught them in this hideous land, they would all most surely die.

So, wearily, and in unutterable discouragement, the men turned about and dragged their way back through Texas and into Arkansas, retracing the route to Guachoya. And their own sins of ravishment met them coming back, for they had taken all the maize and meat they could find in every Indian village along the way. The Spaniards had left the country devastated, and it had not improved in their absence. Now they were confounded. They had never thought of such a thing. Always before they had gone on, had never come back over their route of ruin. Starving Indians were one thing, but starving Spaniards were quite another.

When, incredibly, they found and promptly stole a supply of maize in an Indian town which had been missed before, they located a winter camp above the mouth of the Arkansas River. All the rivers were rising under much heavy rain. Water came up into the camp, higher, higher. The men built rafts and lived upon them, endured a miserable, wet, cold life. Sickness and high water were rampant along the Mississippi.

But there was better timber here to build ships than the party had seen in all the valley. Luis De Moscoso and his men, at least those who were well enough, spent a busy winter on the higher ground. Iron from the rusty slave chains, shot, and whatever else they could find in their possessions which was made of iron, were all heated in a makeshift furnace. Enough of the metal was converted to make spikes and nails. Timber was cut down. Among the men was a Portuguese who had learned to saw lumber in Fez, so he was delegated to take charge of sawing out good, clean planks to build ships. He taught others, who somehow forgot that they were fine gentlemen from Castile and Lisbon. Now they were only desperate men who had to build ships so that they might escape from the Mississippi and the wilderness. It was surprising what a gentleman could do when his life depended upon it!

By June, seven brigantines and their makeshift equipment were somehow finished—seven ships miraculously built on a flooding river, in a land where everything had to be made from what they had left or what they could find nearby. Cables had been fashioned from wild mulberry bark, sails from Indian shawls. The vessels were loaded with supplies . . . all the maize which was obtainable so early in the season . . . pork from the last of De Soto's hogs, cured in salt. All but twenty-two of the horses had been killed and their meat dried in strips. There were 322 Spaniards and one hundred Indian slaves.

On July 2, 1543, the seven amazing ships sailed out of the Arkansas River into the Mississippi and headed downstream with the vicious current . . . down to—what? No one aboard knew, but they hoped it would be the sea.

The Spaniards' troubles soon began again. Indians from warlike Quigaltam came out and attacked from all sides as the ships moved steadily down the river. Indians gathered on the Vicksburg bluffs and rained arrows upon the brigantines. The Spaniards sent out canoe-loads of men to burn the Indian town in retaliation, but barring their way were a hundred canoes full of waiting warriors. They assembled at a little distance, not attacking, but watching every move of the white men.

Luis De Moscoso sent Juan De Guzman, captain of infantry, with twenty-five men in armor, out to drive the Indians away. The Indians let the Spanish come quite near, then divided efficiently into two groups, closed in and neatly capsized all the white men's canoes. The Spaniards fell into the water and, because they wore their heavy, rusty armor, they sank, struggling wildly, to the bottom of the Mississippi mud, where their armor no doubt still lies. A few men clung to the sides of the canoes. The Indians savagely beat at them with clubs and paddles until their desperate, bruised fingers let go and they drowned.

The men on the proceeding brigantines, meanwhile, gazed in horror at this unequal struggle. They could not go back to help, for the force of the current was carrying the ships inexorably onward. Only the last brigantine in the procession happened to be near enough to rescue four of the men. They were all who escaped. Juan De Guzman was gone, among the others.

Next, the Indians attacked the brigantines as they swept frantically past the bluffs, around the bends and down the surging eddies and boiling rapids of Grand Gulf. Only four men on board the ships still had any armor, and the unprotected ones, twenty-five of whom had been wounded in the first volley of arrows which had rained on the defenseless ships, simply let go their oars and fled below decks. The leading ships, unguided, began to swing about broadside in the Mississippi as they were caught in the violent eddies. One of the men in armor forced an infantryman to take the steering oar and right the ship, while he stood close by to protect him with his shield. One after another the seven brigantines went through the fire of arrows and the men aboard could not fight back. But the river proved their friend at last. Its mighty force carried them out of reach of the Indians.

It seemed, however, that they had barely left one area of attack before they entered another, for all the angry Indians in the towns along the way came out to do their worst. In seventeen weary and dangerous days, the ships sailed 720 miles, and they reached the sea at last!

Here the Spaniards decided to follow the shore of the Gulf, around to Mexico. This was a longer journey than it would have been if they had crossed the Gulf, but it was eminently safer for such frail, makeshift vessels. And they all reached a Spanish town in Vera Cruz safely fifty-two days after they left the mouth of the Mississippi. They were heralded as men risen from the dead!

Northward, around the curve of the Gulf of Mexico, a massive volume of water still poured and churned and eddied past the shores where lately a crowd of disheartened, disappointed, gold-seeking Spaniards had come and gone . . . past Indian villages pillaged and burned by the conquerors, who themselves were being conquered by a country and a river, though they would never have admitted it aloud . . . past the place where seven incredible ships with sails made of Indian shawls had pushed out of the mouth of the Arkansas River . . . past the Vicksburg bluffs, past the swamps and sandbars. And somewhere in its depths lay the bones of a man who had brought these interlopers here, and whose dreams and aspirations lay with him in a river which no man would conquer. In the wild swamps and forests, from Florida and the Carolinas westward to Arkansas, roamed descendants of the precious Cuban pigs which De Soto had guarded so carefully, yet could not keep. So, though the Spanish conquerors themselves left no permanent mark, the descendants of their pigs, the lean, wicked razorback hogs of the southern swamps, are still living there today.

CHAPTER FOUR

1673· *"How beautiful the sun is, O Frenchmen,
when you come to visit us."*
JOURNAL OF JACQUES MARQUETTE

THE glory of the maple forests of Canada had burned in their final burst of autumn color, when the two heavily loaded canoes bearing Louis Jolliet and his three friends slid through the cold gray waters of Lake Huron, having come up the St. Lawrence and along Lake Ontario and Lake Erie. The leaves had fallen and snow had begun when, in December, the four men reached Michilimackinac and found Father Jacques Marquette.

The priest was delighted to see his young friend, Louis Jolliet, again. His joy was wonderfully increased when he learned that his Superior, Father Dablon, had given him permission to accompany the expedition on which Jolliet was about to start. At heart, the mild priest was an ardent explorer and woodsman. When he heard the whole story—how M. Talon, the soon-to-retire Intendant of Canada, had selected Jolliet to set out to find the great River *Mese-sebe*, about which the Indians often talked, and to see where it emptied—he could hardly wait to get started.

Although men had been searching ever since Columbus discovered the New World, no one had found a water route across the Americas to the Pacific. Spain, England, France and Holland all needed a short cut to the South Sea, which was their name for the Pacific Ocean. They needed a protected route, a river, perhaps, which would lead ships quickly to the riches of China and Japan, to the great Oriental markets of Europe's merchants. It was with the hope that the mysterious Great River, the Algonquins' *Mese-sebe*, or Mississippi, would empty into the Pacific Ocean, that Louis Jolliet, an expert hydrographer and surveyor, was sent to find out the truth of the situation.

But the expedition could not start so late in the season. Its members put in an endlessly tedious winter at Michilimackinac. The lakes froze, and the ice was a great glare in the low south sun. Snow fell for days and bent the hemlocks. Between snowfalls, the sky was a frigid, pale blue bowl Lake Huron rumbled and crashed when the cold was great, and then shoved up great dikes of expanding ice, like walls, across the lake. In the forests even the owls had a hungry look, when the snowshoe hares, on which they usually fed, died because they could find no more food in the deep drifts.

And then one night there was a different feeling in the air. It was late April. The voices of geese were heard as great flocks flew over in the soft wind from the south. The clouds were low. A fresh smell was everywhere. The lake talked all night, and when morning came, open water lay between the separating ice. In a few days it was scattered in drifting, dark, crumbling floes, which winds from the south soon turned into floating shoals of rotten ice, heaving up and down on the waves. The white gulls

were back, squealing and crying over the water and swooping
down to pick at winter-killed shad on shore. As snow vanished
from the forest, the Indian women began making maple sugar.
The rich, sweet aroma of boiling sap filled the air.

Louis Jolliet went over to Sault Sainte Marie as soon as the
lake would take a canoe, and brought back two more men for
the expedition. He also bought another canoe.

May 15, 1673: Dawn was brightly cold as the sun climbed
above the rim of the great lake and glittered on the pale candles
of new growth coming to the pines. Trailing arbutus was fragrant
in the woods behind the log mission, where another priest had
come to take over Marquette's work until his return from adventure. The two canoes moved cleanly through the blue water, the
paddles digging deeply and not splashing, and in the breast of
Louis Jolliet there rose a beautiful golden bubble of sheer delight. The quiet priest looked at the morning sky and back at the
brown logs of the mission—and at the rough-hewn cross. He
bent his head and murmured a heartfelt prayer.

The voyagers entered Lake Michigan through the Straits of
Mackinac. With a south wind blowing foam and spray, the
canoes were beaten about as they pursued a course along the
north shore of the lake.

After a pause for rest and food with the Wild Rice People at
Mission St. Michael, on the west shore of Green Bay, the party
of six in their two canoes entered the marshy rice beds at the
mouth of the Fox River. It was June 5. Birds flew up in clouds
from the green stalks standing above the water. The way was
easier here, for the travelers were out of the windy, open lake.

At the Mascouten Indian village near the portage between
the Fox River and the Wisconsin, Jolliet looked at his map, but
even without looking at it, he knew what he would see. The
Mascouten village was the western limit of French discoveries.
Beyond here, whatever they saw, wherever they went, would be

new, and whatever they put on their map would be their own discoveries, given to the world!

Two Miamis visiting the Mascoutens offered to show the explorers the way to the portage. The path from river to river was some 2,700 paces long. The men put the canoes on their heads, toted their gear through the aspens and over a foot-trodden trail pricked with deer tracks and came out to the shores of the Wisconsin River at last. The two Miamis, who had left their own canoe on the Fox River side of the portage while they had helped carry loads to the other shore, solemnly lifted their hands in farewell and vanished up the trail.

The Frenchmen silently watched them go. They saw the Indians melt into their surroundings, as a deer does, with no sound or rustling of the aspens or of the hazel bushes.

The Wisconsin River, bright amber, slid swiftly past, glittering in the June sunshine. A black tern flitted low over the sparkles. The current shifted the golden grains of sand on the bottom, which, seen through the clear waters, shone like true gold.

There was a brief prayer; then the seven men silently climbed into the canoes and set off with the current, down the Wisconsin River. These were waters upon which no Frenchman had ever traveled before—or, if he had, he had never come back to tell about it.

Down on the rapid white water, rushing through the canyons called the Wisconsin Dells . . . out into the broader river flowing between sandy hills . . . on . . . on. The trip was smooth and no Indians came in sight.

Early one foggy morning, the water ran more shallowly. Around a large island the canoes surged, and there, there at last, lay the great water the men had sought—the Mississippi River! At that moment the sun burst through the murk, the fog rolled up out of the valley and became clouds in a blue summer sky. The trees covering the great, rounded, rocky cliffs opposite the mouth of the Wisconsin were full of bird songs. The two canoes headed into the big river and turned south.

Louis Jolliet felt like cheering. He felt like standing up and waving his hat, but one didn't do a thing like that in a canoe. Instead, he grinned across the water to Jacques Marquette, who was grinning, too. Louis knew the priest felt the way he did, triumphant and joyful, and maybe a little scared, because no one knew anything much about this big river, not even the Indians, who were only acquainted with small parts of it. Nobody knew either its source or its mouth.

"Let us drink a toast to our success!" suddenly proposed Jolliet. He and the others took their drinking horns and birchbark cups, dipped water from the river and solemnly drank to the good fortune of the expedition.

"To the Mississippi!" cried Jacques Largillier and drank. Then he added proudly, "We alone, of all white men, now have the Mississippi River in our blood!"

When the expedition had gone about one hundred and fifty miles from the mouth of the Wisconsin, Father Marquette began looking for something on the western shore.

"It was somewhere in this country, I believe," mused the priest, "that the Peorias moved when they fled from their base on the River of the Illinois. Some of their people were at Green Bay and Chequamegon, and they told me that a missionary was badly needed in their towns. I promised I would come if I could, and now that I am here, we must keep that promise. Since they are friendly, we shall have our food supply replenished. Besides, a night or two on land, lying flat, will be a great comfort to my bones, as I am sure it will be to yours!" The priest ruefully straightened his stiff back. Sitting in a canoe all day and trying to sleep in it at night was too much for even a young and healthy man. There were times when the thirty-six-year-old

Marquette felt very ancient and decrepit indeed.

"There!" cried the priest suddenly, pointing to the muddy shore. "Human tracks and marks of canoes. Pull over, and we shall follow them. This might be a trail to the Peoria village."

The canoes were paddled to shore. Human footprints were indeed deeply gouged in the soft mud, and there was a glittering of scattered fish scales, which suggested that the Indians had been fishing here.

"If this should be another tribe, a hostile one, then what?" suggested stout Pierre Moreau, who was cook for the party.

"We must risk that," said Jolliet, knowing how deeply the priest felt he must go to find the Peorias. "You will all stay here with the canoes. Walk about and get some exercise while there's a chance, but, as much as possible, take the canoes out on the river and stay there for safety. Father Marquette and I will follow this trail and see where it goes. If we aren't back within five days, then return to civilization and pass the word along to Monsieur Talon that they got us!" He laughed shortly. "But I doubt if you'll need to. We'll be back!"

The priest smiled assuringly. "We shall indeed, God willing," he added.

The two selected gifts from the supply of Indian presents in the canoes and started up the mud-caked river shore to the trail leading to higher ground.

It was several days later when Marquette and Jolliet, carrying a great supply of gifts, came back to the canoes. The two were accompanied by some six hundred Indians—men, women, children and dogs—all following at a respectful distance. Close beside the pair walked a ten-year-old Indian boy, who kept his eyes on the ground. The boy climbed into one canoe with Louis Jolliet, Marquette into the other. The three waved to the assembled Indians on the shore until the canoes had paddled out of sight.

Then Louis Jolliet settled back to tell the others what had

happened.

"For a while I had my doubts about our welcome," he began, "but then they recognized us, and all was well. Some of the Indians here had known the Father up at Chequamegon Bay, on Lake Superior, and you would have been surprised to see how delightedly they welcomed us because of that. An old man who came to greet us with uplifted calumet said solemnly:

" 'How beautiful the sun is, O Frenchmen, when you come to visit us! All our village awaits you, and you shall enter our cabins in peace.'

"They seated us before the chief, in his house. He offered us the calumet, and although that thing tastes pretty badly, you've got to take it and put it to your lips when they offer it, or you're done for! These Indians gave us one to take along; it's like a letter of credit, a passport honored wherever we go.

"When word had gone out to the other village nearby that we had arrived," Jolliet went on, "the inhabitants wanted us to go there, too, so there was nothing to do but to proceed, in great state, in that direction. We were looked at from all sides. Most of these Indians had never seen a white man, and they couldn't stare enough. The whole town went along with us— some going in advance so they could stand to one side and look as we went past, some lying in the grass to stare, some hurrying ahead, then turning and coming toward us so that no detail would escape them. They were completely silent, too, which was a bit alarming. But to them this was a mark of respect, the Father said."

"They had very great reverence for both of us," said Marquette simply.

"Well, we finally reached the second village," resumed Louis, "and were welcomed with great honor, right and left. The chief himself came to greet us. When he heard that we contemplated going down the River Mississippi, he was very much upset. He assured us that there were devils downstream, not to mention most dreadful monsters. I told him we were brave enough to attempt it, but he shook his head at our rashness and predicted no good would come of it."

"Don't forget the dinner, Louis," put in Marquette. "A most remarkable feast!"

"Remarkable!" exclaimed Jolliet with a shudder. "I doubted me I'd live through it. We had four courses—a lot more than you give us, Pierre, but I'll take yours in preference to theirs, any day! Well, we two and the headmen sat in a circle in the chief's house, and the master of ceremonies made it his business to feed us. First he brought in a great wooden platter of *sagamité*, which is cornmeal boiled in water with salt, and seasoned with some sort of strong tasting fat. It wasn't too badly flavored, if you swallowed fast and didn't notice the dirt. The master of ceremonies put big spoonfuls into our mouths, and then watched to see how we enjoyed it, so we had to pretend it was delicious, roll our eyes, smack our lips, grunt, rub our stomachs. We felt like fools. Or I did, anyway."

"I, too, my brother," murmured Marquette with a smile. "I hoped my delicate stomach would not rebel, at least until we got ourselves away from there!"

"They took away the *sagamité* when all had eaten some of it and then came in with another greasy wooden platter on which were three fish that had been roasted in the coals. These weren't bad fare, and besides, the master of ceremonies kindly removed the bones, blew gustily upon the pieces to cool them and carefully, with his fingers, put them into our mouths, as if we were a pair of young owls! We thought we were getting off easily, when in came a third course—a large dog, roasted to a crackling brown! That we just couldn't abide, even if it is a favorite Indian delicacy. As tactfully as we knew how, we informed the chief and the master of ceremonies that in our country we do not eat dogs and consider it against our custom. So the master of ceremonies, not taking it amiss, at a wave of the chief's hand removed the roast, thank heaven! The final course was perhaps best of all—a piece of baked buffalo meat, the fattest morsels of which were torn apart and carefully put into our mouths.

"When we were ready to leave, the Indians brought us gifts. Most of them, as you can see, aren't worth the room they take in the canoes, and I believe we should throw them overboard. All but this one, our little Ouachanon, who was given to me as a slave!

"Ouachanon is the son of the chief," continued Jolliet, smiling at the downcast boy, "and he is surely our finest gift. I doubt me that his mother was very happy to have us take him from her, but I assured the poor woman we would care for her son as one of our own, and promised that, whenever he wishes to return, he will be at liberty to do so. He knows a few words of French—his father was one of the men who visited the missions at Green Bay and Chequamegon." Jolliet bent to look at the boy, whose head had been lowered still more.

"Oh, now, Bibi, you mustn't cry! You'll have adventure— you'll go with us to see where the big river flows. Think of the glory of it; think of the fun you'll have. Smile, Bibi!"

The boy lifted his sober face and fought with the tears that had leaked out of his black eyes.

"It was a beetle flew in my eye," he explained gravely, with a quick wipe of a hand across his face. "I will go with you, my lord."

"That's better," said the young Frenchman in satisfaction, patting the boy's smooth bronze shoulder. His head was shaven, except for a bristling black scalp lock. He wore a breechclout, a string of dog teeth around his neck and embroidered deerskin moccasins.

. "And since you're to go with us as a brother, call me Louis," added Jolliet.

"The chief told us that his people will likely go back to their ancestral village on the Illinois River," Marquette put in. "And he said that, if we wish to take the short way up to Lake Michigan, we should travel up the Illinois. If we do so, then little Ouachanon may return to his people."

The boy frowned and shook his head.

"I stay with you," he declared.

It was June's ending, and the heat of midsummer beat down upon the Mississippi. The days were hot and humid under a scorching sun, and the nights remained uncomfortably warm and sticky, while the mosquitoes punished the travelers both day and night.

The eastern shores were high. They grew higher still as, abruptly, tall white cliffs, curved and channeled by the action of ancient waters, reared aloft. Above them soared bank swallows whose twittering echoed in the rocky hollows.

It was the boy Ouachanon who cried out and pointed, then covered his eyes at the sight of something on a smooth white cliff face. Jolliet turned to look, and Marquette did, too. The men rested on their paddles and stared.

On the vertical rock was the dim figure of a strange creature.

"Do not look, do not look!" moaned the boy. "It is the monster of the river, whose glance kills. My father told me—"

"Hush, Bibi!" said Jolliet sternly, taking the boy's hands away from his frightened black eyes, which were squinched shut. "It is but a picture. Some sort of curious beast is indeed painted there, but that is all. It cannot hurt us. Look and laugh, as we do. See—we are not harmed. Look, Bibi!"

Shaking his head, the boy turned obediently. He glanced hastily in horror, but he could not smile.

"It is the demon of the river," he murmured.

Marquette and Jolliet had been warned of river monsters by every tribe with which they had visited. If this were all—this dimly seen, painted picture of some sort of beast—then the voyage should hold no further terrors.

The pictured creature was as large as a horse. It bore horns like those of a deer, had a pantherlike face and a scaly body with a tail which was so long it passed quite around the body and back between the legs. To Marquette, the thing resembled something done by a Frenchman, not by any Indian. It reminded him, somehow, of dragonlike depictions in France. It puzzled him, as it has puzzled many another man who has passed what later became known as the Piasa Cliffs. But none of them has ever discovered by whom or when the picture was painted.

It was not long after this that the voyagers were startled by the churning of violent rapids on the west side of the Mississippi. They saw an accumulation of large and entire trees, branches, and floating debris pouring from the mouth of a river, the Missouri. Rains up in the distant mountains, a quick run-off in the plains, and the Missouri was roaring full, stirring up its dense yellow mud until the entire river was full of mudboils and looked thick enough to slice with a knife. Through it all the uprooted live trees and the massive dead ones came pounding along like giants on a rampage, catching on each other, piling up in vast rack-heaps, or breaking loose and chewing at the banks, then struggling on into the Mississippi. Five dead buffalo lay tangled in the debris and a crowd of vultures flapped into the air as the two canoes suddenly came upon them.

At this point the Mississippi immediately lost its clarity. It had been losing this slowly ever since the rivers of Illinois and Iowa and Missouri had been pouring prairie mud into it, but none of these were like the Missouri, this great left-hand fork of the Mississippi, born in the mountains of Montana.

Down the river . . . around the vast, sweeping bends, in which it would seem that the explorers were indeed paddling back home again Sometimes the canoes went east, west and north before they managed to turn south again on the broad river. Below the mouth of the Ohio, where the Mississippi became greater than ever, the heat and flies and mosquitoes were worse than before. Now the rocky cliffs were gone. Finally, there were only the red or yellow-brown Chickasaw bluffs, on the east, and, mile upon mile, on and on, willow and cottonwood islands and the swamps of Arkansas. Cormorants sat in rows on bleaching snags, or dived for fish. Vast sandbars lay baking in the summer heat. The river grew low and green and oily-looking. Great brown eddies boiled as if alive, and puffs of brown foam floated past from caving banks.

Now and again an Indian village appeared on the shore. At each one, Jolliet asked the same question:

"How far to the sea?"

Upstream, the Indians had only shaken their heads in reply. None of them had ever been so far, nor had they ever heard of the sea. Hostile tribes, it was rumored, lived down the big river. How far? No one knew.

"What is a sea?" asked Ouachanon. The boy was intelligent. During the long days of slow travel, Jolliet had passed the time in teaching him how to write and how to read, and he was delighted at the way the ten-year-old responded to his instruction. Father Marquette worked with the boy, too, and rejoiced at how fast he learned his catechism, and how sensible were his answers.

"Bibi," Jolliet cried, not answering the question, "when we get to Montreal, you shall go to school there and, God willing, to the college You will be an educated man. With that mind of yours . . . Bibi, you please me!" And the boy beamed at having won approval from the tall young man he so admired.

"And Bibi," went on Jolliet, looking lovingly at the Indian boy, "if you choose to go with me, I shall make you my son when we reach Montreal. You shall have a Christian name and become a gentleman!"

"The boy asked what a sea was," Marquette reminded Jolliet, with a smile at the man's enthusiasm.

"Oh—a sea, Bibi—well, a sea is water so wide you can not see the other shore, and the water is salty, not sweet, nor muddy like this river. And the fishes in the sea are different from river fishes, and very strange and often very big."

At that moment, Marquette's canoe lurched violently as something thudded against its side. A black, shiny tail slapped it. A huge, tar-black shape moved out of sight in the water.

"Holy Mother pray for us!" cried Marquette, holding on to the sides of the canoe. "What was that?"

"A fish, Father," answered Henri Griseaux, laughing. "The biggest catfish I ever saw—as big as a man! It was God's mercy he didn't upset us! You talk of strange, big fish in the sea— well, only think of the strange monsters in this River Mississippi! Who knows what other creatures lurk down in the mud below us?"

On a July day, the party approached an Akamsea village, peopled by a tribe of Quapaws, on the east shore, near the mouth of the Arkansas River. Two long canoes came hurrying out to greet them.

Jolliet raised his calumet and was considerably relieved to see a calumet also raised in one of the approaching canoes. The advance guard escorted the French explorers to shore in state and conducted them to a seat of honor under the chief's sun-awning, which was made of woven cane with green paroquet feathers patterning it.

A feast was hastily prepared which featured delicious, ripe watermelons. The Frenchmen had never tasted them before. In the humid heat of the summer day, these great, cool, pink-meated fruits were wonderfully refreshing.

"How far to the sea?"

"It is less than ten days' journey," answered the Akamsea chief. "But you do not go there, surely? Hostile tribes live below. We do not venture among them. They slaughter without warning. And they trade with men like you who are at the mouth of the Great River . . ."

"Men like us?" echoed Jolliet, taken aback.

"Much like you," amended the Akamsea. "They have Black-gowns such as this one, who call folk to prayer with a little bell, and there are great ships with sails . . ."

"The Spanish!" groaned Jolliet, his big shoulders slumping. He had been fearing this for a long time.

"I thank you," he said politely to the Akamsea, who bowed in return. "You have been highly useful to our pursuit. And now, if you will permit us to hold council among ourselves—"

It was night again along the Mississippi. The reflections of the stars were splashed in the black water sliding sibilantly past the shores. Across the river was the mouth of the Arkansas, a turbulent stream coming from no one knew where. Downstream—now, Jolliet was sure of it—lay the Gulf of Mexico— the Gulf of Mexico and the Spanish!

For some time the young Frenchman had been suspecting it. Daily, with his astronomical instruments, he had determined the latitude of the exploring party. He knew, days ago, that the river could neither empty into the Atlantic in Virginia, as some said it did, nor slant westward enough to strike the South Sea. Jolliet had told no one of his conclusion, but he was nearly sure as to where the Mississippi would empty. Disappointment had grown in him, day by day. France would be disappointed, too!

Jolliet, Marquette and their five companions sat in a close circle. Ouachanon was curled up on a sleeping mat, nearby. The men thought he was asleep, but he was not. Alert as a wild animal, his ears were taking in all the sounds of the southern night—the murmurs from the Akamsea village as it settled itself to sleep, the calls of a chuck-wills-widow coughing in the darkness, the squeak of a bat, the deep-toned rumbling of bullfrogs along the shore, the whispers of the Frenchmen, and . . . and those other whispers, close by. Ouachanon rose quietly to his feet and slid away.

"Father," Jolliet was saying soberly, not noticing the boy's departure, "you may not agree with me, but I must say it. I think we have gone far enough down the Mississippi. It hurts my inmost being to have to turn around now, when we are so close to seeing where the Mississippi enters the sea. It is dreadful to be so close, yet to be in such danger that judgment warns that we must turn back. If it were only my life at stake, I would go on and take whatever risks there might be, but it is more than that. It is not only the lives of my companions, including that of an innocent boy, but it is also our priceless journals and maps, and our knowledge of what we have discovered. Tonight, we are the only Frenchmen—nay, the only white men—in the world, who have followed so far on the River Mississippi and know where it empties. We still do not know its source, but we can be sure of its mouth. It is for us to get back to civilization and tell about what we have discovered—now, quickly—before some accident prevents us."

"You are right, Louis," agreed Father Marquette sadly, because he, like Jolliet, had had his heart set on seeing how the magnificent river finally lost itself in the sea "To fall into the hands of the Spanish would mean death or ignominious captivity. Perhaps we would never return with our information which is so vital to France and all the world. Or, if the savages attack us, we and our journals and maps will be lost forever."

Jolliet laid his weathered brown hand on the black-garbed knee.

"You have put courage into my selfish heart," he said lovingly. "I do not want to return until I have seen the end of the river, but I *must* go back, and you have given me strength to do so. We can be very sure that the Mississippi empties into the Gulf of Mexico, and neither into the Atlantic nor into the South Sea, and that should satisfy us—and the world."

"When do we start?" asked Pierre Moreau, methodically scratching his mosquito bites.

"The day after tomorrow," said Jolliet, with finality. "We will have a day to rest and to make our preparations."

"Good!" cried Marquette. "Tomorrow is Sunday. We shall celebrate the Mass and be able to leave these poor souls somewhat enlightened in the truths of Christianity."

Jolliet stood up. His eyes moved over to the sleeping mat where Ouachanon had lain curled up like a puppy. The mat was empty!

"Where's the boy?" he asked sharply.

Meanwhile, Ouachanon had crept silently as an owl's wings to the whispers he had heard, and listened. Fortunately, they were spoken in a tongue he understood.

"The Frenchmen mean mischief," he heard. "Why do they ask about the mouth of the river and the whereabouts of the sea? I say they are in league with the hated Natchez and are up to no good!"

"True," said another voice. "They must be stopped. Let us cut their throats, then rob them of their belongings. It is no more than they deserve."

Ouachanon listened with a growing horror which turned him cold to his very toes. He didn't know what to do and his heart pounded in fright. Then he remembered what Father Marquette had told him—"when you are in trouble, pray to God and the Blessed Mother," and Ouachanon prayed.

"Oh, God of the white man, help me! Oh, Blessed Mother, hear me!" he whispered.

Immediately, he knew what he must do. The boy hurried through the darkness to the chief's house and rapped at the side of the door. The chief grunted and sat up on his sleeping mat. Ouachanon made bold to creep through the doorway and seat himself close to the Akamsea. He whispered violently of what he had heard. The chief was now thoroughly awake and very angry.

"The evil ones!" he cried. "They would ruin our honor by insulting our guests! Go, boy, and tell the Frenchmen to come to me."

Ouachanon ran.

By the time that he was back with his anxious companions,

the chief had called his councillors and important people of the tribe, and a great fire, leaping into the midnight darkness, was throwing sparks to the stars. When he was sure that all were present, the headman rose. He stood straight and tall and held forth the long, smoking calumet, decorated with ivory-billed woodpecker feathers, in his strong, bronze hands. The drums thudded like hearts beating, and the Indian stepped to their rhythm . . . thud, thud, thud, step, step, step . . . chanting, the calumet held above his head, now presented forward, then high, as if to the sky. The chanting rose to a faster tempo, the drums rolled faster. The chief's splendid brown body glistened in the firelight.

As suddenly as they had begun, the drumbeats stopped, the chanting ceased. The Akamsea moved forward a step. Jolliet got to his feet because he knew instinctively that it was time. The chief presented the smoking calumet to the Frenchman, after putting it to his own lips and drawing smoke from it. Jolliet did likewise and held it respectfully in his hands. No one moved, no one said anything.

Then the chief spoke.

"Frenchmen," said the ruler of the Akamseas sternly. His eyes glinted in the fire's glow and slanted around the gathering of braves as he wondered who had plotted against the guests. "Frenchmen, you and your children and your children's children shall always find welcome, refreshment and shelter in the villages of the Akamseas. Let any who violate this order suffer torture and death. Frenchmen, go now and sleep in peace!"

It was not until Monday, when the canoes were plowing heavily upstream in the sweet, early light of a misty river dawn filled with bird song in all the willows, that Ouachanon told Louis Jolliet what had happened that night. His account explained the men's puzzlement as to why the chief had suddenly called the midnight ceremony, against the power of which no evil could prevail.

Louis Jolliet stared in amazement at the boy, when he had finished his tale. Then he hugged him, almost upsetting the canoe.

"Bibi, how I love you!" he cried.

It was a long, long way up the Mississippi. They traveled in slack water held back by sandbars across the low river, but it was often harder to by-pass the snags and downbound floating trees than it had been to avoid them on the southward trip. The canoers wearily followed the east bank. They were a month traveling from the Akamsea village to the green islands and high hills at the mouth of the Illinois River.

It was easier after the party had turned into this stream. The country was wonderfully beautiful. Herds of buffalo were visible up on the prairies—strange, dark masses, moving in a group, or seen close at hand when they streamed down to the river shores to drink. The lotus seeds in the swamps were ripening by the millions, and beneath them, under the great pale green platters of leaves, hid young wood ducks.

And when the canoes came at last to Peoria Lake, the Frenchmen found that Ouachanon's people had indeed returned to their ancestral village on the hill. Ouachanon's father and mother greeted him with restrained joy.

The boy was torn. He was delighted to see his people, but he was no longer one of them. He had learned to read and to write in a foreign tongue. He had become a Christian. He was—he was different.

"Well, Bibi," said Jolliet sadly, eying him quizzically, "now you must make your choice. I give you back to your father. But if you should want to come with me to Montreal and go to school . . . It is for you to decide."

There was no doubt of the answer. The boy put his brown hand into Jolliet's big, calloused palm and looked up at him with love shining in his black eyes.

"My brother Louis," he said, "I go with you, no matter where —to the ends of the ocean-sea, if you go there!"

The voyagers spent three days with Ouachanon's people, because Father Marquette had promised to stay a bit and preach the faith. There was another pause at the Kaskaskia village, but Jolliet was growing impatient. The little, leather-bound chest in which he kept his journal and maps of discovery weighed upon him. He wanted to get it to Montreal and report his discoveries as quickly as possible.

The travelers veered to the north fork of the Illinois, where it became the Des Plaines, crossed the portage to the Chicago River and came into Lake Michigan. It was the end of September, 1673, before they reached Green Bay, later still when they beached the canoes at Michilimackinac.

Father Marquette was not well. Jolliet was concerned and worried, and he hated to leave until he was certain as to how things went with his friend. Consequently, winter closed down at Michilimackinac, and there he still was.

That winter, the two explorers worked on their journals and maps. It was not until the following July, 1674, that Louis Jolliet, two of his men and Ouachanon finally approached the great city of Montreal, on the St. Lawrence River. Jolliet was more eager than ever to get there, so he decided to take the short-cut, for if they dared to shoot the rapids of Lachine, they would save time; they would gain nearly a day. So into the churning rapids and rocks the canoe plunged.

"Hold tight, Bibi!" cried Jolliet, laughing, working a paddle with the others. He had shot the rapids many times and loved their wildness. It was a rough and exhilarating sport. But this time the canoe hit a rock, capsized, turned completely over.

Jolliet fought the water. . . . It seemed to him that he had been fighting it forever, that he had been always and forever down in the madly churning, icy depths. He struggled to the

surface, snatched a breath, went down, just as he saw Ouachanon's black hair ahead of him. He kicked to the surface again,
grabbed desperately for the hair, but it vanished in the white
foam and he lost it.

It was some time later, he had no idea when, that Jolliet
struggled on to some wet rocks and sprawled there, gasping
deep gulps of air. He felt more nearly dead than he could ever
remember, and as he lay on the rocks, he didn't really care
whether he lived or not. Not now. Not now. Tumbled and
broken at the bottom of the rushing torrent of the St. Lawrence
River lay the precious chest containing his journal and his maps
of the Mississippi River. But even that tragedy didn't matter.
Not now.

Ouachanon was gone! His Bibi, his adopted son, who would
have borne his name and gone to college and been a person of
note. The canoemen were gone, too, but they were men who
dared death daily; it was part of their living, to die. But not the
boy.

When Louis Jolliet finally had an interview with Frontenac,
the new Intendant, he told of what he had found.

"There is no doubt of it," he said flatly, without enthusiasm.
"The Mississippi River flows into the Gulf of Mexico, not into
the South Sea, and there are Spanish ships at the mouth. If I
had my map, I could show you—but it is lost, and my journals.
Excellency, I have failed you. Failed France!"

"But no!" cried the burly Intendant, leaping to his feet and
towering above Jolliet slumped in his chair "You have succeeded admirably. For now we know! We need spend no more
money and men and time in attempting to find the South Sea
by way of the Mississippi. And if you will but try, you can re-
create the map that was lost, for it is still in your head. Sit
down now—I will call for parchment and ink and pen—and
try to remember. Put in all the Indian villages you can recall,
all the tributaries, all the details you had on the other chart
And if you will but dictate what happened on the journey, it

shall be written down again, almost as you had it!"

Louis Jolliet felt a renewed vigor stir inside him. Jacques Marquette still had his rough sketch maps. Everything was not lost—for, once found, no man forgot the Mississippi. He had it in his heart, in his blood. Jolliet had drunk the Mississippi, and he would never forget. He sat down before the shining cherrywood desk and took the pen in his hand.

CHAPTER FIVE

1682: "How dreamwise human glories come and go."
CALDERON

BROWN pelicans flying in formation low above the Gulf of Mexico veered suddenly as they passed over the marshes near the mouth of the Mississippi. A strange crowd of human beings had gathered on that precarious spot. They had planted a column of cypress wood in the mucky earth, had placed with it a rough wooden cross. There was no sound from all the people, save one—a tall and powerful figure that stood beside the column bearing the arms of France and inscribed:

> Louis le Grand, Roi de France et Navarre,
> Regne: Le Neuvième, Avril, 1682

The tall man was speaking. But although his voice was strong, it did not carry very far nor even disturb the pelicans which

55

coasted down to the shore not far away. In a land of vast sea and vast sky, with a channel which was one of three mouths of the Mississippi River lazily pushing its way out into the salt water of the Gulf of Mexico, a human voice was small and impotent.

"In the name of the most high, mighty and invincible and victorious Prince, Louis the Great, by the grace of God King of France and Navarre, fourteenth of that name, I, this ninth day of April, 1682 . . . have taken, and do now take, in the name of his Majesty and of his successors to the crown, possession of this country of Louisiana . . . from the mouth of the great river called the Ohio, as also along the Mississippi and the rivers which discharge themselves thereinto, from its source beyond the country of the Nadouessioux . . . as far as its mouth at the sea, the Gulf of Mexico. . . ."

With these words, in a ceremony which only a handful of people watching understood, for many of them were Indians, Robert Cavelier, the Sieur de La Salle, claimed for France a tremendous accession. It stretched from Texas to the huge valley of the Mississippi, from the Alleghenies to the Rockies, from Canada to Mexico. But aside from the few humans who watched, only the pelicans heard that voice; only the pelicans and the royal terns which flew over, cackling, and the silent, ominous, potent river which had flowed 2,552 miles to reach this lazy ending in the sea.

For La Salle, it was the peak of his heartbreaking career. Never before—and never afterward—had he so much triumph, or so much hope. He was the sort of person to whom disaster seems attracted. A project planned by La Salle almost certainly ran into difficulties, and, in the American wilderness, difficulties were spelled in blood, fire, starvation, freezing and death in its more terrible forms. It was not a land in which failure could be a light thing. But perhaps in all that tremendous wilderness there was no man more persistent in the face of the calamity which steadily trailed his determined footsteps.

Ever since he had come to America in 1666, he had been on fire with the possibilities of the New World. Here was America, he thought, rich in furs and untold mineral wealth, and there was a great river, a pathway of navigation north and south, with a route possible up the Illinois River toward Lake Michigan. It would only require the construction of a canal connecting the Illinois directly with the Chicago River in order to enter Lake Michigan, beyond which lay the route to the St. Lawrence, the Atlantic and France. It would be a splendid, unassailable, two-way route of commerce from the heart of rich America to the ports and markets of Europe. Beaver furs were the great source of wealth at that time and, he thought, much of the traffic in skins could be more profitable if sent directly down the lakes and the Mississippi, instead of via the Hudson's Bay route and the English.

La Salle set about the erection of Fort Crevecoeur, at Lake Peoria, on the Illinois River, where his hand-picked artisans were to start building the first ship for the Mississippi River trade. This would be the beginning of a merchant fleet that would sail down the Illinois and the Mississippi to the Gulf, thence to the West Indies, where larger ships would take the cargo to France.

The whole picture was clear in La Salle's mind. But in reality nothing worked out as he had planned. His workmen had no heart in their labor. There were such fearful dangers of attack by the raiding Iroquois. While La Salle was in Montreal, trying to raise more money for his enterprise, having left his lieutenant, Henri de Tonti, in charge of the fort, the men mutinied. They killed those who remained faithful to the leader, though Tonti and several others managed to escape. The men stole everything they could carry, and threw into the river whatever they could not make way with. They scrawled on the unfinished hull of the ship:

"*Nous sommes tous sauvages. We are all savages.*"

In spite of this disaster, and in spite of the terrible raids of the Iroquois, who were leaving a trail of carnage and cannibalism along the Illinois River, La Salle determined to set out to find the mouth of the Mississippi anyway. Even though he did not have the ship he had planned for, he would travel in canoes and locate a spot for a fort and colony. With the faithful Tonti and thirty other Frenchmen whom La Salle felt he could trust, a hundred Indians and a supply of firearms, the expedition set off in a fleet of canoes, paddling down the Illinois. They reached the Mississippi River on February 6, 1682, a river which was full of massive cakes of floating ice coming down from the north.

Southward went the canoes. They left behind them the dregs of the Illinois winter and entered into springtime. They were swept along on a current bigger than any they had ever known before, as the river neared the sea.

On April 7, they reached the mouth of the Mississippi.

The men made camp on the right bank and erected the arms of the king. It was then that La Salle proclaimed to the listening world that this land now belonged to France. In his mind fermented plans for bringing ships in here, of fortifying the river a few leagues upstream, of settling a thriving French colony, of teaching the Indians how to raise silkworms—in short, to develop America and its resources There was the problem of the Spanish to cope with; but at this moment none of the Spanish, who claimed the Gulf of Mexico as theirs, were anywhere in sight.

The expedition headed back to the fort on the Illinois. La Salle went on to Montreal, where he was laid low by a severe attack of brain fever which threatened both his life and his sanity. He had had other such attacks, and after each one he seemed, to his associates, to be somewhat more irrational in his ideas. Now he went to France to lay his plan before the king.

The plan was this: if Louis XIV would grant him a ship and the men and supplies, La Salle would sail for the Gulf of Mexico.

He would settle a colony above the mouth of the Mississippi, fortify it against the Spanish and pave the way for French shipping and trade up the Mississippi Valley.

The plan came at a time when King Louis XIV was much irritated at the Spanish edict that all foreign ships would be attacked if they entered the Gulf of Mexico. If La Salle could really do as he said, he would defy the Spanish and give France a foothold on the Gulf.

Then La Salle improved on his proposition. He promised to recruit fifteen thousand Indians, even from as far north as Fort St. Louis, on the Illinois River, at Starved Rock, and attack New Biscay, which was northern Mexico. The king thought this was a really splendid idea. It sounded so simple—recruit the Indians, pick up some willing and suitably bloodthirsty buccaneers at Santo Domingo, take along two hundred Frenchmen and a ship with thirty guns and a few cannon for the forts: how could it fail?

La Salle even went so far as to say that, if the venture was not successful within three years, by finding peace with Spain, he himself would refund all the costs to His Majesty.

Mississippi madness had a firm hold on La Salle. It infected the men to whom he talked. They actually believed that the whole wild and insane plan would succeed. The Mississippi, even to people thousands of miles away, was an enchantress forever calling.

The king loaned the Sieur de La Salle four ships. They were named the *Jolie*, the *Aimable*, the *Belle* and the *St. François*, the latter carrying most of the equipment and supplies. Many men—mechanics, laborers, gentlemen, adventurers—came along. There were some families for colonization, as well as a number of girls who were lured by the romance of helping to start a new colony undoubtedly containing more men than women. There were missionaries, also, including La Salle's brother, Cavelier, a Sulpician priest, with two others of that order, as

well as three Recollects, among them Father Anastase Douay.
A scholar named Joutel kept a journal of the expedition. From
him, we learn something of what happened.

Two months after the group embarked—and after a dismal
voyage during which there was much illness—the ships landed
at Santo Domingo, off the island of Cuba, to take on supplies.
Only three vessels now comprised the fleet. The fourth, the little
St. François, had been captured by the Spanish It was a disas-
trous loss. After a prolonged stay on the island, during which
time La Salle was very ill again, the three ships set out, with
La Salle on the *Aimable* leading the way. They followed the
south shore of Cuba, then headed confidently at a slant northwest, so as to strike the mouth of the Mississippi River.

And they could not find it. They overshot the mark. Perhaps
they passed it in the night. On New Year's Day, they anchored
three leagues from shore and La Salle and some of the others
landed to explore and get their bearings. They found nothing
but a marshy wilderness, full of muskrat huts and wild geese
and brown canes bending in the Gulf wind. Returning to the
ships, they coasted along to the west, straining their eyes to
see the mouth of the great river which would bring them their
fortunes. And still they could not find it.

On January 6, 1685, a wide opening was discovered between
two points of land; mud discolored the sea water.
"There! There it is! The Mississippi at last!" cried La Salle.
In his relief, tears started from his bloodshot eyes. No man
had ever seen any such sight before. It was as if the leader
looked on the face of a loved one after a long, long absence.
But it was not the Mississippi River. It was Galveston Bay,
in Texas. Nor was it the mouth of the Mississippi that they
navigated when, in desperation because food and water were
low, they reached Matagorda Bay and resolved to land. La Salle,

in the growing disorder of his mind, was sure that this was it, and he directed the *Aimable* to enter the bay. But the *Aimable* was wrecked on a sand bar. Fortunately, however, nearly everyone from it and the other two ships managed to get ashore.

The adventurers were an unhappy lot. They were ill and many were dying of dysentery. Gales tossed fragments of the wrecked ship on shore, and from them the people half-heartedly attempted to fashion shelter. Indians harassed them from the rear and set grass fires. When, on March 12, Captain Beaujeau departed with the *Jolie*, he was worried about the dreadful situation he was leaving behind him. He asked La Salle if he wanted him to send supplies from Martinique before he returned to France, but La Salle refused. When the *Jolie* had vanished beyond the horizon, the Sieur de La Salle had but one ship left for his escape. And when the *Belle* was wrecked in a storm shortly afterward, there was no longer any means of escape by sea . . . not unless the king sent out a ship to find the lost colony. But only Captain Beaujeau knew of its location, and after his rebuff from La Salle, he was not likely to come back.

La Salle wearily directed the construction of a larger fort. He ordered gardens planted. But even in more comfortable quarters and with better food, the people were dying. Meanwhile, La Salle could not forget the great river. He was still obsessed with finding the Mississippi. Night and day, it called to him. It seemed incredible that he had lost it. Often he and some of his best men went out from the makeshift colony in search of the river, only to come back weeks later, thwarted, and always having lost some of the men and supplies along the way.

Discontent and mutiny brewed among the unhappy people. Those who plotted against La Salle were reputable men— Doctor Lanquetot, a business man named DuHaut and several others, including a not too reputable buccaneer named Hein from Santo Domingo.

When La Salle and his Indian guide, Nika, the scribe, Joutel,

the priests Douay and Cavelier, and several others once more
set out to try to find the Mississippi, the plotters followed. At
the first night's camp, they ruthlessly shot down the Indian,
Nika, and when La Salle heard the shots and came running to
see what had happened, he met a bullet head on. The Sieur
de La Salle crumpled upon the cruel, parched earth of Texas.

His brother in horror saw the leveled guns of the three
murderers, then dropped to his knees, waiting for his own
death. Father Anastase Douay, oblivious of what might happen
to himself, knelt beside the body of the leader and devotedly
and selflessly recited the prayers of the Office of the Dead.
The murderers spared the two priests and Joutel, but they would
not permit them to bury La Salle's body. The three assassins
boldly helped themselves to his clothing and guns because they
were so desperately needed. They left the explorer's body to
the vultures.

The death of La Salle and new leadership made little stir in
the colony. So many dreadful things had happened to the deserted people that one more death had little meaning. But now
the triumphant plotters determined to find the Mississippi themselves and escape from this terrible land. So they left the pitiful
remnant of betrayed people at the fort in Texas, forced Douay,
Cavelier and Joutel to accompany them. They hit off across the
country until they came to the Arkansas River at last.

But, as they camped beside the river, using the hospitality
of an Indian village, the buccaneer's conscience began to hurt
him. He felt he was in the company of evil men, felt it his duty
to serve Doctor Lanquetot and Monsieur DuHaut as they had
served La Salle. With these two murdered, the buccaneer, nevertheless, felt he might be safer with Indians than with Frenchmen. Consequently, it was only the faithful Joutel, chronicler
of the expedition, and the two priests who came at last to the
Mississippi, there at the mouth of the Arkansas. After a long
and weary journey they reached Fort St. Louis on the Illinois,

where they told Tonti all that had happened—all, that is, except for the death of La Salle. They felt they must keep this silent for morale purposes, at least until the king was informed.

But Tonti was wise in the ways of the wilderness, knew what it did to men. In alarm, he and a party of Canadians and Indians hurried down the Mississippi and ranged along the coast to look for his beloved friend and his settlement, but they could not find him nor any trace of the lost colony. They had not gone far enough west. Returning up the river, Tonti left a letter for La Salle with the chief of an Indian village.

When King Louis XIV heard of the failure of the expedition, he shrugged and frowned, but he did not send out a ship to rescue the remnants of the colony, though Captain Beaujeau could have led such an expedition. Who cared? The king turned to other matters. Texas and the Mississippi were too far away for him to comprehend.

Indians and the Spanish contrived to wipe out the last of that earliest French colony west of the great river. But the Mississippi still called, and other Frenchmen were to answer.

CHAPTER SIX

1699. *"I have come back, my river,
I have returned to you."*
                    SYLVESTER

On New Year's Day, 1699, two French frigates left Santo Domingo and steered north. The commander, Pierre Le Moyne, the Sieur d'Iberville, was determined to succeed where La Salle had failed. He would find the mouth of the Mississippi. Iberville and his brother, Bienville, had read carefully all the accounts of those who had gone before them—the journals of Marquette and Jolliet, of Joutel and Hennepin—so that he felt certain he could not miss that strangely hidden mouth of so great a river.

With him at the rail of the ship stood Father Anastase Douay, the weathered Recollect friar who had survived the La Salle tragedy and who was coming back again because the Mississippi would not let him rest. The friar leaned on the ship's railing and let his eyes follow the sea northward. The waters were curiously brilliant, banded with emerald and turquoise and purple, where troops of glistening black porpoises leaped in graceful arcs and vanished in the color.

They cast anchor in the lee of Ship Island, south of the present city of Biloxi, Mississippi, where the wind lay low and the red-beaked skimmers yapped in the mild sunshine. Ashore, the party found a peaceful village of Biloxi Indians who stared wide-eyed at the white men. Iberville tried to make them understand what he wanted—the river, where was the Great River? How should he reach its mouth?

They had never heard of it. They shook their heads and shrugged their shoulders.

But there were some Bayagoulas, far from their own towns, visiting the Biloxis. They came forward and let the Frenchmen know that they indeed were acquainted with the Great River, for they and their people lived beside it. It was westward, toward the setting sun, and was very large.

West! So he had not missed it, after all. Unlike La Salle, who had gone too far, Iberville had yet to come to the mysterious river which was so big that Frenchmen couldn't find it.

The Bayagoulas would not go with the French, but told them to follow the shore, to follow it wherever it took them, and they would surely come to the mouth of the river they sought.

The French left the ships anchored where they were and set out in two small boats to trace the shore. It took them south and west, among many islands, then almost due south, so that Iberville began to lose heart, not knowing that the delta had shoved a tongue of land out into the sea. He felt that somehow he, like La Salle, had missed the Mississippi and now was following the curve of the Mexican coast.

On the morning of March 2, 1699, the boats came to a body

of water spreading itself through muddy marshes which were on a level with the sea, marshes green with cane and loud with the cackling of millions of white terns which got up in alarm as the two small boats went by. Mud poured with the turbid liquid far out into the clear gulf water, and the men, tasting it, found it fresh and not salty. There was a chance that this was indeed the Mississippi, but they had seen so many streams pouring into the gulf, so many mazes in the strange sea-level marshes, that no one, not even Anastase Douay, could be sure.

The men could see nothing but the water winding ahead of them, the endless expanse of cane and willows where glossy, long-tailed blackbirds scolded and sang. Pelicans sailed above, turning their heads to watch, and flocks of thousands of plovers passed overhead, going north. Iberville grew impatient at being able to see nothing but the monotonous shore, the vast sky and the brown water. There appeared to be no proper land, only low cane marshes for many miles, then cypress swamps standing tall, rising from the dark water and hung with strange gray streamers of moss.

"Do you think this can be the Mississippi?" he asked Anastase Douay a dozen times a day, and the priest could only shake his head.

"If it is, I do not remember this part of it," he said apologetically.

Iberville was culling his brain for all he had read of the writings of Hennepin and Joutel and Tonti, but he could not remember, exactly. It could be, or it could not be, and if not, then *where were they?*

A hundred miles or so up the river, the water turned in a great curve, and both Iberville and Bienville spoke at the same time. "A perfect place for a fort!" And then broke into a laugh as they saw how they had thought alike.

"A fort built here, and a colony, would guard the whole upper Mississippi," Iberville continued, on fire with imagining as this slightly higher ground, after all the miles of dreary swamp, inspired him with planning.

Bienville went ahead in his boat, then paddled back to say he had come to an outlet leading to the east which might possibly carry them back to the gulf by a shorter route.

"Excellent!" cried Iberville. "But first let us make certain that we are indeed upon the Mississippi and not upon some other stream. We will explore tributaries later. Now, on to the north —or as much northward as this crooked river takes us! Methinks we are traveling west and east and north and south on all these curves and bends. Never have I seen the like!"

The river took them near the village of the friendly Bayagoulas, who welcomed them with a peaceful calumet, feasted them on roasted fish and happily took the presents offered in return.

"There once were other white men," the chief said slowly, "who spoke as you, and dressed as you. One gave me this cloak."

He proudly displayed the garment. Bienville gave an exclamation and felt the cloth with his hands. It was good wool serge, and no Indian had wool cloth without his having obtained it from a European.

"Where did you get this?" he cried.

"A white man such as you," again said the chief of the Bayagoulas calmly. "They call him Tonti, and all Indians know and love him. None would do him harm, not even the Iroquois, they say."

If the chief had said the name of the King of France himself, the explorers would have been no less delighted than they were to hear that magic name—Tonti. Henri de Tonti's peculiar personal magnetism captivated white men and Indians alike. They all revered him, all admired him, stood amazed at his courage among the most hostile tribes. Tonti could go from one end of the American wilderness to the other, and no Indian would harm him, as the Bayagoula chief had said. And Tonti, the beloved Tonti, had been here. The delighted Iberville was sure, now, that he was right—this must be the Mississippi.

But Hennepin's account had made no mention of the big bend of the river nor of the Bayagoula village.

Anastase Douay had no doubts. His face was shining with inner joy. He, too, knew of Tonti of the Iron Hand, and he, himself, was completely certain that they were now on the Mississippi. There was an aroma from the brown, eddying, ever-changing, moving waters, a power which cast its spell over him as it had done before. For he, like Father Marquette and Louis Jolliet, long ago had drunk the water of the Mississippi and would have it forever in his blood.

"I would not follow too closely what the good Father Hennepin says," Douay remarked placidly, watching the river slide past the village of the Bayagoulas. "He was not always—exactly accurate," the priest added tactfully.

"Humph!" snorted Bienville, throwing down Hennepin's book. "Accurate! All Europe says the Recollect was a liar. The things he says! I suspected it before and now I am sure. Hennepin was never at the mouth of the Mississippi. He simply stole La Salle's account, twisted it to suit his fancy and bungled it terribly."

"Before we pass judgment on the Recollect or on our location," put in Iberville judicially, "we shall proceed northward and make certain for ourselves."

They found villages of the Houma Indians where the maps of Jolliet and Joutel placed them. They found a palisaded camp with a temple inside built of upright logs and smoothly plastered with mud. A conical roof was thatched with canes which were painted with curious figures. Around this strange temple there were at least two hundred cabins, built of logs and cane. And in the Houma village Iberville found a glass bottle.

It had been placed in the temple with other valuable sacred objects.

"This bottle," began Iberville in excitement, "where did you get it?"

"The man called Tonti gave it to us," said the Houma chief proudly. "Tonti himself was here many moons ago."

Tonti again. The trail was growing hot.

With some of the Houmas as guides, the explorers came at last to a shore on which was a tree trunk painted red, with heads of alligator gar, catfish, gaspergou and bear hung upon it.

"This is the boundary between the lands of the Houmas and the Tunicas," the interpreter explained. "They call it the Red Stick—we should say Le Baton Rouge—" And so the spot was always called, even much later, when a Louisiana town was built upon the site of this boundary between two fierce Indian tribes.

It was in a village of the Taensas, however, that Iberville experienced his greatest excitement.

"There is a chief who dwells somewhere near the mouth of the Great River," said the Indian slowly, "who has a piece of bark with talking words upon it. Tonti gave this to him. The chief says that Tonti told him to give it to a Frenchman who would come up the river from the sea."

"Does the chief still possess this letter?" cried Iberville, in mounting eagerness.

"I cannot say," said the chief of the Taensas carelessly, dismissing the subject. "Many moons ago I heard that he was still waiting for the Frenchman to come, but it has been a very long time . . . and who knows what has happened now?"

This was all that Iberville and Bienville needed to make them turn around and head back down the river. They stopped at the Indian villages along the way, inquiring always for Tonti's letter, but no one knew anything about it. When they finally reached the outlet to the east which they had noticed as they rounded the big bend coming up, and which was suspected to be a route to the sea, Iberville and his boat turned into it to explore.

"We must make the most of our time," he said regretfully, "and although I would prefer to find Tonti's letter, if it ever existed, it is more practical that we find an easy way to the sea. I shall attempt to reach the ships from this route, while you proceed on our former route down the river and thence to the ships, as we came. Now God be with us all, and let us meet again!"

Anastase Douay prayed, and the men bowed their heads and were blessed. Then Iberville and his boat proceeded upon the unknown bayou channel, going southeast. Eventually, they came into a great body of water which was not the sea, but which lay near it. A few years later it would be given the name of Lake Pontchartrain.

Meanwhile, Bienville made more inquiries for the letter as he went down what everyone now was certain must be the Mississippi. He had not much hope of finding the document, though. La Salle, for whom it doubtless had been intended, had died in a strange land, and many years had passed since Tonti expected his friend to receive the missive left behind for him. Perhaps, too, the whole thing was a fable, invented by the Taensas chief to send the Frenchmen away from his own village.

At an Indian village where they halted for provisions, however, he once more asked about a letter.

The chief shook his head, but his eyes were veiled.

"The talking bark left by the Sieur de Tonti for the Frenchman who never came?" repeated Bienville, smiling in his most winning manner at the old Indian, who, nevertheless, did not smile back nor soften. Bienville reached into his packsack and brought out a fine hatchet.

"For this, will you exchange the letter?" he asked.

The chief's weathered brown hand reached out for the hatchet. He examined it carefully, feeling the edge with his thumb. Then his face grew more friendly. He went into his house and brought out a roll of soft deerskin. Unwrapping this, he held out a piece of bark on which were faded words . . . words in French, directed to the Sieur de La Salle, and signed by Tonti.

Everyone in the party of explorers felt glad, and somehow

solemn, at finding the long lost letter to the dead La Salle, because now they knew that they had done what La Salle and the others had failed to do. They had indeed discovered the way into the Mississippi from the sea—and who knew what possibilities their discovery opened in the continent for New France and the king?

Six weeks after the exploring party left the ships anchored at Ship Island, Bienville and his men were paddling out of the mouth of the Mississippi and into the gulf. At the same time, Iberville and his men were paddling across Lake Pontchartrain and into Lake Borgne, then out into the Gulf of Mexico at the Rigolets Pass. The two parties reached the ships only an hour or two apart. They were full of tales of their discoveries. Chief among them was the news of Tonti's letter, but of more permanent and vital value was the assurance that Iberville and his men had indeed found the way to enter the Mississippi from the Gulf of Mexico. They had found the way in, and the foothold of France on the Great River now was certain.

John Law

CHAPTER SEVEN

1715: "Southward through Eden ran a river large—"
                                                    JOHN MILTON

IN 1715, the old king of France died. Louis XIV, whose heavy
hand and ignorance of America did so much to influence the
New World and the Mississippi, had finally bowed out. He
left France and its colonies terribly in debt. During his last
years, Louis had desperately urged Iberville to find profitable
mines and furs in New France, in order to defray that debt;
but, in spite of the king's orders, one could not wrest great
wealth so quickly from a wilderness so large. The French king
simply could not comprehend the vast distances in America,
nor the constant dangers and difficulties with Indians which
hampered progress in colonizing, mining and searching out the
wealth of a huge, virgin land.

When the grand state funeral was over, Louis XV succeeded Louis le Grand. But the new king was only a small boy, five years old, so his uncle, the Duke of Orleans, became regent, to rule in his place until little Louis attained the years and wisdom which one felt were necessary to be a king. The pleasure-loving regent did not find the going as easy as he had anticipated. His country was still as greatly in need of quick money as it had been before the old king's death.

Three years earlier, Louis XIV had given to one Antoine Crozat a monopoly on all Louisiana trade for fifteen years. This privilege included the sole ownership of all the mines he might discover, so that the wealth of America might be properly channeled and profitably developed. But five years later, the bleak outlook in the Mississippi Valley was growing steadily worse, instead of better, as far as gold, jewels and furs were concerned. Iberville was dead in Cuba. Bienville was doing his best to keep a colony going at Biloxi and another at Mobile, the capital of Louisiana, though everything—weather, finances and people—seemed against him. Crozat had lost more money than he had gained from the faraway Louisiana country.

In disgust, he handed his monopoly back to the regent, thankfully and with good riddance. Crozat was astounded when the exiled Scottish financier, John Law, stepped in to develop the Mississippi himself.

"But it is an impossible country!" cried Crozat to Law in exasperation. "Everyone has talked about the gold and jewels, but where are they? I have seen none of them, nor has anyone else, except in his imagination. Louisiana is a miserable land; it is full of swamps and snakes and mosquitoes, not to mention murderous savages. It is broiling hot or freezing cold; always the Mississippi torments a man. Summer and winter, it is never good. No settlements can ever be permanent in America, especially along that barbaric river!"

"Ah, so?" commented handsome John Law, and smiled quizzically at the disturbed little man.

"Yes! Besides," went on Crozat in injured tones, "the leaders are always quarreling and doing nothing constructive. They sit about all day, hating each other, hating the country, hating that hideous, muddy river, a stream too wild of current even to permit any man to venture to discover its source—imagine! They detest me, too, for sending them out there—all but Bienville, who is doing the best he can and professes actually to like America and that river! It is getting so I can't even persuade idiots to go out to the Mississippi; they would prefer the deepest dungeons of the Bastille to Louisiana. So what can I do?" He shrugged expressively and rolled his eyes.

"Why not, then, have picked better men?" asked John Law casually, looking down from his splendid height at fat little Crozat. "All that the Mississippi country wants is good men with energy, brains and imagination to see success in the swamps and wealth in the woods. We need a city out there, a seat of government better than miserable Mobile or Biloxi. And we must send out the right men to govern it!"

"Ah, but if I could have done that, my fortune would have been made!" sighed Crozat, slapping his forehead and beginning to pace. "No one will go! They say it is the equal to being condemned to the galleys, to death itself. They'll jump overboard first. If it isn't the Indians, it's disease, and if it isn't starvation, it is floods and hurricanes. Most men of sense would choose the gallows to the Mississippi, I tell you. I fear I am of the same opinion. I wouldn't set foot in Louisiana for any amount of money! I wish you luck in your venture," he added sourly.

But the other was only half-listening. "I will make the Mississippi so desirable," mused John Law, smiling to himself, "that men will pay to go out there, will give me their fortunes to buy land in that most wonderful country along the beauteous River Mississippi!"

"You mean that you really are going to take over—*Louisiana?*"

cried Crozat, brought up short, aghast yet irritated at the handsome young man's assumption of success where he, Crozat, had failed.

"The Duke of Orleans and I have now formulated the Company of the West. The duke has given me the exclusive rights of trading on the Mississippi for twenty-five years," said Law carelessly, examining his fingernails. "He has given me the monopoly of the beaver trade of Canada, so that, instead of the furs going down the Great Lakes and the St. Lawrence to Montreal and Quebec, they will come down the Mississippi—many bateaux loaded with precious, soft brown furs! You recall that not long ago there came fifteen thousand skins by this route.

"And we will build a splendid city down near the mouth of the river to receive our exports. Tell me, how many people are in your colony, Monsieur Crozat?"

"Scarcely more than three hundred," admitted Crozat glumly.

"Heavens, man, what have you been doing these five years?" Law laughed, rubbing together his slender, skillful, gambler's hands. "Watch me! Watch Louisiana! Watch the Mississippi! I wager we shall give you plenty to talk about!"

France watched. France talked. John Law was attempting to put money back into the depleted French treasury by a special system of his own, which consisted largely of outlawing gold and silver money and replacing it with paper money. He was so successful at it that he was made Minister of Finance. Then his Company of the West began to develop the Mississippi. It sold shares in the Mississippi Valley, shares which rose higher and higher in price as inflation grew greater. Land was bought and sold and bought again without any real money having passed between the hands of the frenzied buyers. The Mississippi was put on the market in France; but, although the sale vastly influenced that entire nation and its people, the river was unconcerned at the furor and quite unchanged as it carried men's destinies on its turbid brown waters.

In the Bank of France, meanwhile, there soon came to be more paper money than there was gold. No one thought of that except a few worried financiers who cannily took their own cash to safety in Holland and Belgium before the inevitable crash. John Law was printing up millions of banknotes, and everyone was joyfully, spendthriftily rich.

The Mississippi Colony, however, was John Law's pet project. He is believed never to have visited America, but the big river nevertheless called to him, and it relentlessly caused his eventual ruin. In an excess of enthusiasm, he sent out people to the Louisiana settlement. He ordered a city built in 1718. He had the elaborate plans drawn up for it. Bienville was directed to start work at the best and most strategic spot for a colony, as well as to build a fort to protect French interests on the river. The town, Law said, would be named for the regent, the Duke of Orleans . . . New Orleans.

In 1718, Bienville, now Commandant of Louisiana, set about clearing and surveying that certain higher land at the great curve of the Mississippi which he and his brother, Iberville, had thought so long ago would be ideal for a fort and colony. The banks were ten feet above the river—little enough, to be sure, and it overflowed them readily enough in time of flood. To the east, the land sloped away swampily to Lake Pontchartrain; the workmen and new residents were troubled with alligators, snakes and mosquitoes. There were moss-draped cypresses with jagged knees to be felled and grubbed out of the ancient muck. Their wood was tough and fibrous; it dulled many an ax. There were jungles of tall cane to be hacked down and burned. The ground was always soggy. All in all, it really seemed to be a most unlikely spot for a city of any duration.

Yet, in a land that was predominantly marshy for more than a hundred miles up the river from the gulf, this was the best location, and it was imperative now to have a fort here. Storehouses and cabins for traders were built. Three companies of infantry and a small group of hopeful French families landed in

March, 1718. Late in the steamy summer, when the river was low and almost gravy-thick, three hundred more settlers came, lured by promises of ease and freedom. They arrived in time to be laid low with swamp fevers.

During the following spring, five hundred Negroes from the Guinea coast of Africa were unloaded from the foul-smelling hold of the ship in which they had suffered for months in crossing to America. In October . . . a large group of Germans and Alsatians came to settle on John Law's own grant of land, at the mouth of the Arkansas River

The financier, however, wasn't satisfied with the progress of his colony To advertise it, pamphlets and papers were printed and widely distributed, illustrated with engravings of the beautiful landscape of America. The pictures featured neat, smiling Indians, kneeling to the French and giving them a multitude of fine gifts. John Law evidently had borrowed some of Sir Walter Raleigh's descriptions of Virginia, had added a few more interesting touches, including that durable fairy tale about streets of gold and jewels scattered carelessly about. He published a plan of the new city, which appeared to the dazzled eyes of beholders as the grandest city in the world.

Yet, in spite of the ballyhoo, people of the right sort were slow in coming forward to colonize in that splendid paradise along the Mississippi. They might buy and sell during the "Mississippi Bubble" frenzy, but colonizing was a different matter. It suggested discomforts which were not at all attractive to people accustomed to Paris and civilization. But Law needed people. He could not realize his plans without them. He needed men to dig in his mines and fish for pearls, men to plant rice and corn and wheat and indigo and tobacco, artisans to build his cities and merchants to carry on trade with the Indians, who were still the biggest purveyors of beaver furs So, for want of volunteers, he stooped to taking convicts from the prisons, pairing them up, man and woman, and having them married on the spot, then shipped out to New Orleans. He emptied orphanages to add to the population of his city. He sent out everyone he could persuade, cajole, bully, threaten, or capture John Law even obtained a decree from the always agreeable Duke of Orleans that, if servants were dismissed, they must receive on the day of their dismissal a certificate of good conduct and character and must find a new position within four days. Otherwise, as idlers and vagabonds, they were promptly sent off to the Mississippi!

America in those days, consequently, was being populated largely by the dregs of France, by unwilling men and women and children, shipped out to what often became their doom. Deaths were numerous. And the people who came to what had been proclaimed the finest city of the New World found only a few miserable huts squatting in the mud. Around it a vast and menacing river curved like one of the snakes whose bite caused other deaths in that terrible spot, which had looked so good on paper and in John Law's fine and well-chosen words.

Yet John Law and his Company of the West brought more than six thousand white people to the Mississippi Valley, and some three thousand Negro slaves. Even though New Orleans was slow in developing into the city he visualized, it eventually grew into the Queen City, pride of the Mississippi and the South.

Colonization was one thing, development another, John Law was discovering. The latter needed experts. To hunt out and work the mines of the new land, John Law sent one of his picked men, one Philippe Renault, the director-general of mining operations. Renault left France with two hundred miners, to dig precious stones and metals along the Mississippi. On their way to America the ship stopped at Santo Domingo, in the Caribbean, so that Renault could purchase five hundred slaves. Many of these were brought north, up the Mississippi, to endure— or perish in—the cold winters of America and the upper river.

Renault's people built the town of Prairie du Rocher, in Illinois, which still stands, now four miles distant from the Mississippi. It was the upper-river headquarters for Law's Company of the West. Along much of the length of the Mississippi, Renault's prospectors and miners hunted treasure. More matter-of-factly, and lacking gold and diamonds, Renault set them to mining lead. This was sent down the Mississippi from northern Illinois, Iowa and Missouri, to be loaded aboard ships going to France— lead to make bullets for France's wars.

Meanwhile, back in France, speculation was going wild. Shares in the Mississippi Valley were rising higher and higher, until at last the mania reached its limit. Servants had become richer than their former masters. Rich men were growing wealthier over night. There was a demand for everything fine and expensive; objects were bought simply because they were costly and everyone had money to spend. Prices of food and other commodities went higher still. There was too much paper money and not enough cash behind it.

Suddenly, public distrust started a run on the Bank of France. Paper money was exchanged for gold until no more was left. Panic began when the money ended. Men were ruined in twenty-four hours. Shares in the Mississippi country dropped . . . and dropped . . . and dropped. Ruination replaced the beautiful dream in the mind of John Law, who, even at that distance, had a love for the compelling river. The "Mississippi Bubble" burst.

France was nearly bankrupt again. John Law was exiled. The Mississippi colony had to manage the best it could. And New Orleans, that miserable cluster of cane-thatched log cabins in the swamp, on the day when John Law's "Bubble" was shattering into a million glittering pieces, was being battered by a rising wind off the Gulf of Mexico.

The cypresses flung their lacy greenery, then snapped off, sending moss and branches flying. The palmettos tore in shreds, and sand blew, and canes in the marshes bent double. Birds flapped to cover. Pelicans struggled in the gale. Rain began and the wind roared, blowing everything horizontally. People were killed by flying debris as the log houses came apart in the hurricane, and pieces of the clay chimneys flew off into the storm. New Orleans, such as it was, was leveled. So were the French towns of Biloxi and most of Mobile.

But they were rebuilt, and in 1722 the French government in Louisiana was transferred from the unpleasant situation at Mobile to the somewhat less miserable one at New Orleans. By August, Bienville had taken up residence in the new capital, which had had streets laid out in it, though they were so muddy that one traveled with difficulty until sidewalks of planks were laid down. . . . Life along the Mississippi, for the moment, looked hopeful once more to the weary Bienville and his people.

CHAPTER EIGHT

1805: *"The Mississippi River takes its rise in divers lakes which are in the country of the people of the north."*

JOLLIET

AND still no one knew exactly where and how the Mississippi River had its beginning. Mile by mile, shore by shore, the river had become better known as a watery highway from New Orleans and the Gulf of Mexico to the Falls of St. Anthony and the Minnesota fur-trading posts. But beyond that—from whence did the river flow? From what inexhaustible fountain did it find its perpetual strength and power?

In 1700, Du Charleville, kinsman of Bienville, wanted to attempt to extend trade connections farther to the north by following the Mississippi to its source. He traveled some distance beyond the Falls of St. Anthony. When the Sioux, however, mischievously told him that the source was as far from the falls as was the distance from the falls to the sea, Du Charleville gave up in alarm, which pleased the Sioux mightily. Du Charleville reported to Bienville at Mobile that the beginning of the Great River lay far north, near the Frozen Ocean, that it would be hopeless to try to reach it, and no man, doubtless, would ever attain that goal.

And yet, the question was still there in the minds of many thoughtful men: *where is the source of the Mississippi?* It was a gnawing question, an uneasiness which would give them no rest until it was solved. It was like reading the end of a thrilling story and ignoring the beginning; of knowing the maturity without knowing the birth

There came a time when an invisible line was drawn down the middle of the Mississippi, making one half of it Spanish and the other half French. The French half, however, soon became British almost all the way to the sea. The boundary was drawn to the headwaters—and there again that nagging question came up for the thousandth time: where *is* the source of the Mississippi? Its correct location might mean important things to several nations. If it lay far enough north, it was part of Canada and hence under the jurisdiction of the British, who were touchy to deal with in the great fur companies up there. If the source lay in the lands of the hostile Sioux, there could be problems in that situation, too. Who knew? No white men had gone all the way and thus settled the question forever.

Not until Napoleon sold the Mississippi and his vast Louisiana Territory west of it to the United States, in 1803, was anything concrete done about actually exploring the newly acquired lands and determining exactly where all its wonders lay. Then the Lewis and Clark expedition was sent out to follow the Missouri to its source; and, in 1805, youthful, red-haired Lieutenant Zebulon Montgomery Pike was commissioned to find the source of the Mississippi.

It was August when Pike, his twenty young soldiers and his supplies embarked from the muddy waterfront of St. Louis. A crowd of people gathered to watch the seventy-two-foot keelboat let out its large square sail to take advantage of a hot south wind. With hurrahs and a volley of shots, the keelboat set off up the Mississippi, bound . . . where?

The upper Mississippi was considerably different to navigate than the broad reaches of the lower river, below St. Louis. The upper was a maze of channels which wound lazily through marshes and among islands, and because in late summer the river was very low, the party often went astray in the winding labyrinths of swamp and spent hours finding the way out again. Sometimes the soldiers had to leave their oars and leap out to shove the heavy keelboat off a sandbar or mass of drift.

The expedition hit the Des Moines Rapids above Keokuk on August 20. The rough water sent them back downstream before they could row to the side and contemplate this unforeseen obstacle. Somehow, Zeb Pike had visualized sailing or rowing placidly up a broad river. No one had told him of these rapids which, in low water, apparently extended for miles upstream in shoals and rocky ridges. Men and boat struggled along for hours until, on the shore, they spied a village of Sac Indians. If they were unfriendly, it would only add to the woes of blistered palms and sore muscles of the laboring soldiers at the hickory oars.

Thankfully, they watched a canoe come out from shore bearing a white man who was the Indian agent for the area. With him were Indians who cordially offered to help the keelboat through the rapids. The Sacs unloaded some of the heavy barrels of supplies into their canoes, and, with the vessel lightened, they all finally got it above the rapids and reloaded it.

The party was again on its way, rowing northward, using the sail whenever possible, when they began to see the first hint of autumn color coming to sapling maples and poplars on the banks. Except for a lack of fresh meat, the trip was going well.

"Look!" cried one of the men suddenly, pointing to shore. "Indians! Maybe they'll sell us some meat!"

"Excellent!" cried Pike enthusiastically. "Row toward shore and we'll parley with them. We are still in the country of the Sacs; the agent downstream assured me they are all friendly."

As the keelboat shoved toward the bank, four Sac men and two women, incredibly dirty, stared from the edge of the trees.

"We need meat!" called out Pike loudly, believing that, if he raised his voice, they would be more apt to understand what he said. How he wished that he had thought to bring an interpreter along!

"Meat! Venison!" he said and made motions of putting food in his mouth, rubbing his stomach, casting his eyes hungrily to the sky.

The Indians still stared. One of the women grinned behind her dirty hand and nudged her companion.

"Give them whiskey," suggested one of the soldiers.

"Better water it down, though," warned another. "If we give 'em too much of it, we won't have near enough to last us till this merry trip is over!"

So the little jug of whisky was well diluted with river water, taken from the far side of the boat, and two men went ashore with Pike to give it to the party of Sacs. Instead of receiving anything in exchange for the gift, however, the white men got nothing but dull-witted stares and head-shakings. The whiskey, meanwhile, was spirited from sight.

As the keelboat shoved back into midstream, there came loud and raucous shouts from shore. Pike turned in alarm and the soldiers let out a volley of imprecations and groans. The gleeful Indians, who had understood all that had been said, were capering about and waving two haunches of deer meat—and the jug of whiskey. They were shouting in vast, savage joy at how they had fooled the stupid white men.

September came, and with it a growing blaze of color on the autumn hills of Iowa and Wisconsin. There was a pause at Julien Dubuque's lead mines, another pause of some length at Prairie du Chien, where Zebulon Pike hired a French-Indian named Rousseau to go along as an interpreter. The incident downstream had soured the lieutenant on trying to travel without one. He also exchanged the unwieldy keelboat for two small boats.

It was fortunate that the burly, ruddy-cheeked, black-bearded Rousseau came along. Not far above Prairie du Chien the party approached the first Sioux village on the Mississippi. A sudden rain of bullets and yelling savages leaping about on shore made the startled young soldiers back water.

"No, no!" screamed Rousseau, who had listened to what was in the yells on shore. "It is that they are welcoming us. They greet us with joy, too much joy. Hey, you sons of dogs, cease the firing! You will kill us with your welcoming. Hola! Stop it! *Cessez, vite!*"

Chief Wa-basha staggered to the shore, raised an unsteady hand of welcome; the braves reluctantly stopped firing. In their delight at preparing a cordial reception for the expedition, news of which had come from Prairie du Chien, they had drunk too much and now were in a state of inebriation which threatened to turn the party into a shooting fray. Cautiously, Pike and his men landed, with Rousseau haranguing Wa-basha at a great rate and scolding him for the way his braves had acted. The chief abjectly apologized.

After a feast and entertainment in Wa-basha's lodge, the expedition was on its way again. A raw north wind was blowing out of a gray sky, across a gray river, and yellow leaves came showering down from the birches and aspens on the hills. Geese in long skeins, southward bound, patterned the sky.

The wind was roaring when they reached the broad stretches of Lake Pepin. Rousseau, who knew this treacherous lake-in-the-river, warned the party not to attempt to cross it by day.

"Wait until night, my frien's," he insisted. "Then the wind ceases to blow; he rests, and while he rests, we make good time!"

They camped on the windy shore and made fires to cook their dinner. Darkness fell early on that autumn day, and while the last lemon glow of the sun still lay in the west, there rose out of the east a great burnished autumnal moon which put a broad avenue of shimmering light across the rough waters of Lake Pepin. The hills on the eastern shore were the blacker for the coming of the moon, but the lake seemed to pick up its light and cast it upward into the air, so that there was a frosty glimmering everywhere. Under its spell, the worried young soldiers relaxed. They brought out their violins and flutes and tuned up as best they could in the chill, damp air. Music danced from the strings and the pipes.

"Hola! Put up the fiddles and come!" ordered Rousseau peremptorily, and Pike tardily repeated the order. Rousseau took many privileges, since he was so experienced in this north country, and Pike made no mention of his forwardness, but was honestly thankful for his guidance.

Laughing, the soldiers hastily packed up their food and fiddles, but while some bent to the oars of the two boats, the others continued their singing and playing. They could not help it. The moon did it to them, and besides, they were young.

But the wind had not died. It had only crouched, waiting. It sprang at them violently, and Rousseau broke off in the middle of the sixteenth rousing chorus of *Allouette* to grab an oar, too. The wind roared and waves leaped, cross currents made hazards. Somehow, they did not know quite how, the frightened young men got the boats safely into a protected bay and, panting as if wolves were after them, beached them so that they would not be carried away by the wind. The group camped there for the night. Clouds came over the moon and the night grew black and full of violence.

By morning, the storm was kicking up great spume-tossed waves on the ice-gray expanse of Lake Pepin. There was so much flying mist and spray in the air that the far shore was almost invisible. Still, Pike urged them on. He could feel the approach of winter and he knew they must get a shelter built in a strategic spot before its terrible northern icy grip, of which he had heard, became reality.

Eventually, the party traversed the river-lake and continued up the narrowing Mississippi. They camped one day on an island which later was named Pike Island and is still there, below the present site of St. Paul–Minneapolis. A Sioux village sent up smokes from the mainland.

Mindful of his official instructions, Pike called a gathering of Sioux chiefs of the neighborhood. After a lengthy and intricate parley—during which Rousseau interpreted violently, with much waving of hands, rolling of eyes and shrugging of shoulders—a treaty was signed in which the Sioux permitted the United States to purchase 100,000 acres lying on either side of the river (now most of the area occupied by the Twin Cities). The treaty stipulated that the Indians might pass and repass, hunt and make other use of the area. As a site for a fort, Pike bought the land for two hundred dollars' worth of trade goods. Some time later, when General Wilkinson, Pike's commanding officer, heard of this transaction, he was outraged.

"Too extravagant by far!" he sputtered. "Do you think this nation is made of money?"

However, a few years afterward, on this same spot, Fort Snelling was built and it still stands as a great military reservation. And what of the Twin Cities, bought for two hundred dollars in cheap knives, beads, mirrors and whiskey? Pike purchased better than he knew.

A little way up the narrowing, rocky-cliffed river lay that impediment to navigation, St. Anthony's Falls. After sending his final farewells by letter, with a messenger, down the river to St. Louis, Pike set out on the last desperate stretch of the expedition. If he found the source of the Mississippi, men would never forget his name, never.

The men carried the boats overland for a distance, to avoid the falls and the swift current above and below. When they put the craft in the water again, they were traversing a Mississippi River which went winding through prairie marshes and low woods, through a puzzling maze of islands and shallow water. Sometimes, in order to get through at all, the men had to climb out in the cold water and wade for hours, until they were numb, pushing and pulling the boats. In early October, rains set in, and it grew so cold at night that the temperature fell nearly to zero. There was plenty of meat, however. Buffalo were shot along the shore, and there were always deer, fine and fat, and ducks and geese to vary the menu. Each day some of the men went ashore and roamed all day, hunting, then meeting the party at the nightly camp. Each man ate seven to eight pounds of meat every day and it took a lot of hunting to keep the rugged explorers filled.

The cold increased. It was difficult to keep warm at night. Pike's ink froze in the bottle before he could get his journal written. Snow began in mid-October, and then the important thing was, not to find the source of this dwindling, miserable, endless river, but to get to a place where the party could build a fort for the winter.

It was a race against time to reach the Crow Wing River, said to be a good location for a camp. Pike wondered for the thousandth time why he had chosen so late a season in the year to come north. If he had waited until spring . . . but it was too late to regret that now. His responsibility was to see to the welfare of his men. Already some of them were unwell and unable to go on. They had, therefore, to stop short of Crow Wing River and set up camp instead at Swan River, near what is now Little Falls, Minnesota. They built a hasty stockade and shelter house. The country round about was fine and well wooded, with plenty of pine for huts and boats. But the lone little party was fifteen hundred miles from St. Louis. As misfortunes set in, the men felt farther and farther from the surety and comfort of civilization. St. Louis might be at the end of the world, for all the help they could get from it.

And now it was December 10, deep winter in the Minnesota country. With his men provided for, Pike was still obsessed with that prime mission—to find the source of the Mississippi. By now, the river was partly frozen, so, with a goodly quantity of venison provided for each soldier at the fort and for those who were to go along, Pike and eleven of his best men, together with the hearty Rousseau, to whom no hardship seemed unbearable, set off on foot through the forests to the northwest.

Two large sleds were built to haul supplies. Each of these was pulled by two soldiers, harnessed abreast. Six others dragged the two canoes. They toted two barrels of provisions, which weighed some four hundred pounds, loaded on each sled.

Winter swirled out of the north. Snow, more snow, howling winds blowing blizzard-flakes horizontally out of the northwest, the air stinging like an assault of stilettos, the pines moaning and hissing, their needles hanging dry and parched in the cold. When the river at last froze solid, the sleds were taken on the ice. This was easier than trying to break a way across rough and trackless swamp country and through the forests.

On Christmas Eve, the men had never felt so alone or so cold or so unhappy in their lives. They were at the site of the present-day Brainerd, Minnesota, and still persistently following the meandering Mississippi. Pike, doing the best he could in honor of the great feast day, handed out extra meat and flour, and doubled the rations of whiskey and tobacco. But it didn't help much in a country that was a stark wilderness of rocks and snow, bare trees and frozen lakes, lakes everywhere, each one a sheet of ice rimmed with bare tamaracks, black swamp spruces, or the lumpy hummocks of muskeg. The Canada jays whined in the pines and flew down to salvage meat scraps at the camp.

As the expedition at last neared the American Fur Company's post on Sandy Lake, two miles from the Mississippi, the men moved inland and paused there for a rest. Here at last, for the first time during that dreadful winter, Zebulon Pike and his men knew what it was to be warm and comfortable and cared for, their frosted fingers and toes doctored, and plenty of warm food in their stomachs.

Here Pike hired a Chippewa guide, for, to be so close to what he felt was his goal and stay inactive, though in comfort, irked Zebulon Pike as the days of January went by and they still lingered at Sandy Lake. The men were in no hurry to move on, but Zeb Pike felt the pull of the Mississippi calling to him. He had to go and find out, now, at once, before the year 1806 grew any older. He *must* solve the eternal mystery of the river's source.

And so the party followed the narrowing Mississippi as it turned in a curve northwest, like a frozen fish-hook. The Chippewa guide, meanwhile, regretting his rash decision to take the crazy white men to find where the Great River had its beginning—a foolish enough pursuit for winter time—deserted and went back to the warmth and comfort of Sandy Lake Fur Post.

The twisting little river rambled through a maze of more frozen lakes. Now and then there was a thunderous, rending sound, as a tree split in the great cold. There was little game to be seen, only the white snowshoe hares drifting in dizzy circles when they were startled from among the balsams. There were no birds but the little piping chickadees which seemed quite unaware that the temperature in Zeb Pike's precious thermometer stood far below zero, and that the wind, fresh off the Arctic Circle, cut like a knife.

At last the men came to a place where the Mississippi appeared to fork. To the right, Pike had been told, lay the way into Lake Winnibigoshish, which he felt was the end of that fork. To the left, however, lay a longer river and this, he was sure, was the Mississippi. It was the route to Leech Lake, and, as Rousseau had assured Pike:

"The Indians, they say that Leech Lake, she is the true source of the Mississipp'."

The river—it was really Leech Lake River, not the Mississippi at all—led into the big body of water called Leech Lake. Pike, on February 1, 1806, looked out across the ice that was covered with windrows of snow, and felt a surge of almost painful triumph in his heart. He was there. He had reached the ultimate height of the Mississippi River! It had been given to him to have the privilege of revealing the source to the world, which had never been sure of it before.

"I will not attempt to describe my feeling on the accomplishment of my voyage," he wrote, "for this is the main source of the Mississippi."

Zebulon Pike left an American flag flying on the wintery shores of Leech Lake, and the weary, half-frozen men departed from what they were so sure was the origin of the Great River.

CHAPTER NINE

1832: ". . . *meandering with a mazy motion*
Through wood and dale the sacred river ran."
                                        COLERIDGE

LIEUTENANT ZEBULON PIKE wrote up the notes of his expedition and they were published. In New York, a few years later, a young man named Henry Rowe Schoolcraft, a geologist, came across this report and read it with a mounting excitement in his heart.

He examined Pike's maps, compared them with old and most recent ones. He read the lieutenant's careful notes again. Then Schoolcraft leaned back in his chair and let out his breath.

"The source of the Mississippi!" he exclaimed aloud. "The source? No—*not* Leech Lake—he didn't go far enough! Pike was wrong. If only I—"

Schoolcraft's chance came, years later, when he was appointed mineralogist on Governor Lewis Cass's expedition to explore the Minnesota country, newly come under the governor's jurisdiction.

Schoolcraft joined big, burly, jovial Governor Cass at Detroit, in the spring of 1820. The governor had readied the materials for the journey, but was impatiently waiting for the leisurely Chippewas, up on Lake Huron, to deliver the three big birch canoes which he had ordered weeks before.

These craft were thirty feet long and six feet wide. They could carry about four tons loaded, including complete materials for their repairs, as well as baggage, and eight men who paddled at four miles an hour. Schoolcraft, to whom everything in the Middle West was new and wonderful, marveled at the adaptability of the birch canoe for river and lake travel.

On May 24, 1820, the expedition was ready to go. The three canoes were loaded, the French-Canadian voyageurs, Indians, and soldiers were impatient to start. A large gathering of people watched the departure, and held their breaths as the enormous bulk of Governor Cass was lowered into a canoe. It went down alarmingly until some of the baggage was shifted.

June 7—a pause at Michilimackinac to take on supplies . . . June 18—Lake Superior . . . July 5—the western limits of Lake Superior . . . July 17—Sandy Lake trading post, two miles from the Mississippi.

From this point, some of the group set out in three canoes, with provisions enough for no more than twelve days. Lewis Cass went along. He had rested a bit at the post, was showing a surprising stamina and endurance and seemed actually to be losing some of his great weight under the strenuous life and plain food.

To Henry Schoolcraft, the entire expedition before this day had led up to the moment when he set out upon the infant Mississippi. This, to his own mind, was the real meaning for the whole trip. . . to find the source of the Mississippi. The dreadful tamarack swamps they had traversed, the storms on the big lakes, the long days in the heat—they were only the preliminaries to the dedication of his mission—to find where the river rose . . . the river, the river, always the river.

From the American Fur Company trading post, the little Sandy Lake River took the canoes quickly, in two short miles, to the Mississippi. In this comparatively narrow stream, so unlike the river at St. Louis and at New Orleans, Henry Schoolcraft felt a potent meaning. The young Mississippi . . . he was getting nearer and nearer to its unknown birthplace. There was a strong current and there were many rapids. The river was sixty yards wide, the shallows filled with bullrushes, wild rice and willows. The water was clear, the yellow-brown sands glittering with particles of mica.

On the night of July 19 it was so cold that water froze on the bottoms of the overturned canoes at the camp and laid a scale of ice as thick as a knife-blade on everything wet. A heavy fog in the morning rose slowly, to permit the men to see only a little way.

Above the Rapids of Pokagama, it was as if the Mississippi finally had reached a level, for it flowed gently through a wet prairie which was so covered with tall grass, wild rice and rushes that the men in the canoes could not see above it. The river wound endlessly and turned to all points of the compass in the same hour. For a while they paddled nine miles by the windings of the river, but advanced only a mile in direct line. They appeared lost in the endless marsh of waving grasses. Crowds of black terns flew up, cackling excitedly and sometimes darting down to strike at the heads of the men in the canoes. Redwinged blackbirds scolded and trilled from the waving reeds, and the small, dark-headed Franklin's gulls flew up in alarm as the canoes went past their nesting places in the great marsh. There were ducks and herons and marsh hawks, and the men, simply in the relief of looking at something besides the big sky and the grasses that margined their world, watched the birds.

And so one day they approached the fork in the river at which Zebulon Pike, a few years earlier, had turned to the left. Even in New York, Schoolcraft had disagreed with this, so he now persuaded Cass to lead the expedition on to the right . . . following thirty-five miles of clear, winding river, to Little Lake Winnibigoshish, which was so shallow and muddy of bottom that it was navigated with difficulty. Governor Cass was beginning to believe that they had indeed taken the wrong turn, when the other side of the lake was reached, and with it a channel which Schoolcraft insisted must be the Mississippi. So they followed this for ten miles and came to another lake, Big Lake Winnibigoshish. They crossed it, with even more difficulty than they had encountered on the other lake, and camped, worn out and disheartened, on the north shore.

Next day, the leaders had to make the difficult decision as to which of the streams flowing into the lake was the Mississippi. Was it Round Lake River, Turtle Portage River, Thornberry River . . . or that other branch? And this latter they chose. It led them finally into Upper Red Cedar Lake.

"Here we arrived at 3 p.m. on July 21st," wrote Schoolcraft. "This may be considered the true source of the Mississippi River . . ." But Schoolcraft, in his very wording of the report, showed his own doubt.

Lewis Cass, however, was content. He was weary of sitting all day in a canoe and watching the wild rice and bullrushes go past his head. Besides, he felt they had indeed come to the beginning of the Mississippi River.

"We must rename this lake," Captain Douglas was saying, as everyone stood there, looking at the body of water out of which flowed the stream they had been following for so long. "Since there are other Red Cedar Lakes, we must give this one at the source of the Mississippi a more important name. Why not Cassina Lake, in your honor, sir?"

This delighted the stalwart governor. Beaming down from his

more than six feet, he looked at Captain Douglas and at Henry Schoolcraft and at the beautiful lake with its star-shaped island and was most pleased with the name.

But Schoolcraft, unaccountably, was not happy. He felt deep down that they had not gone far enough. The Indians were telling him about how there were two tributaries flowing into Cassina Lake—Turtle River, which originated somewhere up near the Rainy Lakes, and River La Beesh, which came six days' journey by canoe west-northwest from Lake La Beesh . . . a small lake and not important. . . . West-northwest . . . Lake La Beesh . . . the thought drummed in his brain as he lay awake on his balsam-bough bed that night.

Henry Schoolcraft continued to think about the river.

"Estimating the distance to Lake La Beesh, at sixty miles," he wrote in his journal, "we have a result of three thousand thirty-eight miles as the entire length of this wonderful river which extends over the surface of the earth in a direct line more than half the distance from the Arctic Circle to the Equator. It is also deserving of remark that its sources lie in a region of almost perpetual winter, while it enters the Ocean under the latitude of perpetual verdure . . . and as if disdaining to terminate its career as other large rivers do, has protruded its banks into the Gulf of Mexico more than a hundred miles beyond any other part of the main. To have visited both the source and the mouth of this celebrated stream falls to the lot of few, and I believe there is no person living beside myself, to whom the remark can now be made. On July 10, 1819, I passed out of the mouth of the Mississippi in a brig bound for New York, and little thinking I should soon revisit its waters, yet on the 21st of July of the following year, I found myself seated in an Indian canoe, upon its source."

By September, the expedition was back at Detroit. No men had been killed, none were seriously hurt or ill. They had traveled some five thousand miles and had seen what many men had never seen. . . . They had found the source of the Mississippi . . . or had they?

Henry Rowe Schoolcraft's restless, inquiring mind was plagued by doubts. He was too polite to contradict his chief (Schoolcraft had been paid $1.50 a day for his services as a mineralogist, not as advisor to the governor). One day he would go back to find out for himself where that little River La Beesh came from . . . to find the *true* source of the Mississippi.

Slowly, by inches, his chance was coming. He was appointed Indian agent of the Chippewas and lived above St Mary's River, at Sault Sainte Marie. Here he wrote books on the customs of the Chippewas, from which Henry Wadsworth Longfellow drew his basic material for the epic poem, "Hiawatha." Rewarding though all this was, Schoolcraft still was plagued by the Mississippi's mystery.

Then in 1832 the chance came at last. Not an order to find out the true source of the river—it was believed to have been found already and had been duly named for Governor Cass. No, Schoolcraft was to proceed to the country at the head of the Mississippi, to visit as many Indians as possible, to look after the Indian trade and, in particular, to find out how the Hudson's Bay traders were trespassing upon American lands. He was to vaccinate the Indians wherever possible. But he was not told to explore. No one mentioned the Mississippi.

Schoolcraft departed happily, with Lieutenant James Allen and a small detachment of soldiers as escort, and reached Cassina Lake (now called Cass Lake) on July 10, 1832, twelve years after his first visit. He had an Indian guide called Ozawindib, the Yellowhead, who told him he was right—the Mississippi River truly went on and had its source in little Lake La Beesh. He, the Yellowhead, had followed it and had seen the source many times.

So the Yellowhead collected five small canoes and made all

the necessary preparations. The party started out on July 11, traveled up the little Mississippi River, out of Cassina Lake and into Lake Bemidji. At its southern end, a narrowing little stream, too shallow in midsummer even for small Indian canoes, angled west and south. For a distance the group portaged, and came at last to a shining body of water out of which tumbled a small, glass-clear, cold little stream only a few yards wide.

"This, sir," said the Yellowhead simply, while the black terns cackled and the tamaracks and swamp spruces fluttered their needles in the breeze, "this is where the Great River has its birth. Here, truly, at this spot."

The Yellowhead had been so sure of their destination before they came here that Henry Schoolcraft had been working on a name. There was a missionary named Boutwell accompanying the party, looking for a good place to found a mission. He knew some Latin, so between them they worked out a name meaning *true source*—*veritas*, for truth, and *caput* for head. Boutwell couldn't remember the Latin for 'source.' But that would do it. Schoolcraft carefully shortened the words, so that *veritas caput* became *itas-ca*. The result was Itasca, which could very well have been an Indian name, but was not. It was born at that instant, on the day when the white men stood for the first time at the spot where the Mississippi has its origin.

Lieutenant Allen and his men erected a flagpole made of a tall, thin tamarack stripped of its branches, and the American flag snapped out splendidly in the breeze, making the terns veer in alarm above its bright colors. Schoolcraft felt that great sense of awe which comes to a man when he knows he is experiencing something deep and momentous and incomparable. This was it. He knew. He had found it. *Veritas caput*—Itasca, the true source.

Now, from Lake Itasca to the Gulf of Mexico, a distance of 2,552 miles, down a continental slant of 1,475 feet, a slant as high as six Niagaras, the Mississippi River at last was known all the way by Americans. The big river had always been American. No Spaniard, Frenchman, or Briton could ever have changed that. But this was the first time it was known and acknowledged, for its entire length, as American, by Americans. It was a great moment in the ancient river's career.

CHAPTER TEN

1811: ". . . *the steamboats were finer than anything*
on shore . . . they were indubitably magnificent,
they were 'palaces.' . . ."

CLEMENS

THE first steamboat to navigate the Mississippi did so with
more difficulties, dangers, horrors, excitement, superstition and
downright unbelievable happenings than any other steamboat
ever encountered. When that first craft plied the Big Waters,
the river thrashed about and reversed its current, swallowed islands, collapsed its shores and apparently did its best to devour
this stubborn, bright blue, impossible, noisy little vessel. Coinci-
dence was being overworked when the Mississippi met its first
steamboat on the day of its worst catastrophe.

That little, accident-beset steamboat was not the first to be built. Men had been experimenting with the curiously powerful substance called steam for a long time before they found out some of the things it was good for. To make it propel a boat, however, was cause for scornful laughter. People laughed long and hard when a poor benighted dreamer and inventor (which amounted to the same thing, folk said) named John Fitch built a boat run by steam. It actually moved under its own power on the Delaware River, in 1786. It was a crazy sort of thing, everyone agreed, watching in fascination and waiting for the explosion. It didn't come, but John Fitch wasn't satisfied with his steamboat, so in 1791 he built another. This was more successful and had more speed than his first one. His engine was so strong that the odd small puffing boat ran from Philadelphia to Burlington, New Jersey, twenty miles one way, and actually carried a few people who were bold enough to risk their lives on this new mode of transportation. It wouldn't last, onlookers predicted, watching the little boat shudder under the thudding of her palpitating engine. Nothing could replace sails.

John Fitch was ahead of his time. Ridicule, lack of funds and no financial support for his invention preyed upon his mind. One day Poor John Fitch, as people called him, killed himself. But he couldn't kill the steam engine.

A few years later, a young man named Robert Fulton picked up Fitch's plans and studied them. He knew a little about steam and about boats, and from the plans he thought he saw a way to develop a workable steamboat. He combined some of the best points of other unsuccessful craft and produced one of his own. Robert Fulton, therefore, was not the actual inventor of the steamboat, although the legend of his having done so is an inerasable part of American tradition, along with George Washington's cherry tree and Ben Franklin's kite.

Fulton's *Clermont* was a beautiful craft, built like a small ocean-going ship, with a deep keel and fine, sleek lines. She was painted blue and had masts and sails for good measure, to give people confidence. Folk agreed that she looked very pretty on the

Hudson River. Some felt that the *Clermont's* speed of five miles an hour was excessive. They would trust themselves in this boat, however, much sooner than in Poor John Fitch's thrown together affair.

As early as 1807, men were already wondering how Fulton's new type of vessel would serve on the inland rivers. They were such violent streams as compared with the quiet, deep, eastern rivers. The *Clermont* did well on the Hudson and the Delaware, but would she or a sister ship do as well on the Mississippi or on the Ohio?

Nicholas Roosevelt, a New York financier, was interested. He went west, and from a flatboat, he and his wife took soundings on the Ohio and on the Mississippi. When he returned, he and Fulton planned a steamboat for the Mississippi which might solve the problems of more or less one-way travel on the western rivers, and would bring about transportation and communication between the isolated frontier communities.

By the fateful year of 1811, Robert Fulton and his backer, Chancellor Livingston of New York, and the Fulton-Livingston Steamboat Company, had readied their first Mississippi River boat. It had been built at Pittsburgh and was named the *New Orleans*, in honor of the hoped-for goal, more than two thousand miles away. She was a pretty ship, built like a small schooner, with portholes in her hull and two cabins in the seven-foot hold. In addition to a smokestack, there were two masts with sails, for safety in case the steam engine failed, or to assist if the wind was right.

The *New Orleans* was looked upon with awe and wonderment. This was mingled with a large degree of doubt as she left Pittsburgh, with Nicholas Roosevelt and his indomitable wife aboard, bound for the Mississippi and New Orleans.

In four days the steamboat successfully traveled, with considerable noise of engines and puffing black smoke, down the Ohio as far as Louisville. Below Louisville lay the angry ridge of rocks across the river which formed the Falls of the Ohio.

When the water was high, it completely covered the rocks so that navigation across them was easy. The river was much too low now, in late November, for any boat of deep draft to pass safely over the Falls, much less a boat built with the lines of an ocean ship. When Nick Roosevelt was taking soundings before the *New Orleans* was built, he must have done so during high water. So the *New Orleans* waited.

While she waited, several strange things were happening in the Great Valley. They seemed to be quite unrelated. The brilliant comet of 1811, night after night, was blazing across the sky. This was disquieting enough; many people were alarmed with dreadful forebodings of disaster.

Meanwhile, keelboat men were coming from the Mississippi with tales about the strange way in which the squirrels were killing themselves, committing suicide, droves of them. They were trooping across country, through the woods and over the prairies, and were unaccountably throwing themselves into the river Some swam to shore, but hundreds, thousands, perhaps, had been drowned, and for miles you could see their floating bodies.

Yes, it was a peculiar thing, people agreed. And so was the way in which water, early in December, came up muddied and roiled from the bottoms of once-clear wells, over in Missouri and Illinois and in Kentucky and Tennessee, especially near the Mississippi. It didn't look right. It was downright queer Something was bound to happen with all those signs and omens.

And meanwhile, the little sky-blue steamboat, the *New Orleans*, waited at Louisville. Mrs. Roosevelt's baby was born on board. Everyone was impatient to be on his way down the rivers, if they were going to do it at all.

Finally, in early December, there was a big storm up in Pennsylvania and West Virginia, and the Ohio felt a surge of water. Suddenly, the captain of the *New Orleans* couldn't see the rocks in the Falls of the Ohio, nor even the current of water swirling over them. It was all high water now. Smoking fearfully, her paddles frantically spinning in the foam, the *New Orleans* headed southwest down the Ohio to the Mississippi.

Indians, here and there, looked in fright at the strange, noisy craft churning up the waters of the rivers. This creature was a bad omen, they said, shaking their heads, like the comet in the sky and the squirrels . . .

For a long time the circuit riders had been preaching the end of the world, so that on the cold, frightening night of December 16, 1811, a good many people in the Middle West were sure that the time had come at last. At two o'clock in the morning, it happened. The people in log cabins in the area around New Madrid, Missouri, located on a bluff above the Mississippi, were tossed out of bed with a thump and the hideous certainty that the world was indeed coming to a dreadful end—and they with it.

Chimneys fell in, roof-timbers cracked. Out of doors, there was a wild tumult of landslides and horrifyingly loud rumblings and explosions, as the earth belched forth large volumes of sand, water and sulphurous gases. The earth rose and fell in sickening waves. Houses and animals and people were swallowed in great cracks which opened as if to receive them and then convulsively closed. The bed of the Mississippi shifted, gaped, filled, writhed. Waves beat frantically against banks which were caving in with a vast and thunderous sound of doom. As the current turned back upon itself and surged madly upstream, part of the Missouri town of New Madrid slid into the river. The old shore-line was completely changed, boats sank and were never seen again, nor their crews, and where land over in Tennessee dropped in, a new lake formed. It was called Reelfoot Lake, because a club-footed Chickasaw chieftain, legend said, was buried in it with his bride.

Awful though it all was to the survivors of the New Madrid area—and for miles around to a somewhat lesser degree—no one knew at the time that they were all enduring one of the worst non-volcanic earthquakes in the history of mankind. There had been other bad earth-shakings in the Mississippi Valley, the Indians recalled, but surely none so bad as this. It must have been caused by the comet and the strange, noisy, water-walking boat—that bright blue, smoke-belching monster, the steamboat *New Orleans*.

It did seem a trifle coincidental that the *New Orleans* should encounter such a terrible cataclysm shortly after setting her paddlewheels into the Mississippi The steamboat churned slowly and fearfully through the tumult. The river was in a constant turmoil. The channel was all changed. The shores were unrecognizable to the poor harassed pilot who was doing his best to navigate a new and untried craft safely through a dread, unknown river. It was as if he had never seen it before in his life, he complained sadly, though he had navigated keelboats on the Mississippi for years and had felt he knew it well.

Islands which had been his landmarks had sunk; new islands were forming before his eyes. The river was making desperate cut-offs in the big bends, through which the water was rushing twice as fast as normally. Trees floating on the waves formed murderous weapons when they rammed his ship. The pilot did not attempt to navigate at night, but when morning came, he never knew if he would find the boat still tied to the tree around which he had looped his lines the night before. Tree and bank might be washed away, leaving the boat wallowing at all angles, or dragging a line attached to a tree long since fallen in and lying forty feet below on the deep-sunken bottom.

Through it all, the new little Roosevelt baby managed quite well. The other passengers and crew grimly held onto their sanity and hoped to get to New Orleans. It was impossible to go back. They had to go on. But they could hardly have chosen a worse time to make the maiden voyage of the first Mississippi steamboat.

After the great quake, the situation eased a trifle, though the shaking continued at intervals. An enterprising Kentuckian who

kept careful note of the shocks recorded 1,874 separate earthquakes in the following three months, before the earth subsided
and let men and river rest.

Before the telegraph, word traveled slowly. It was some time
before even the news of the extent of the earthquake reached
the East. At last, up the rivers, came word of the *New Orleans*.
She had indeed, slowly and with much trouble, somehow reached
her destination, on January 10, 1812. And there she stayed. She
was unable to return north. Her engine was too weak and her
draft much too deep for anything but fairly high water. Bound
upstream, with only that little engine to shove her forward, she
knew she would never make it. The steamboat stayed around the
city of New Orleans, however, and carried people over short
distances, as far north as Baton Rouge, where deep water ended.

In July, 1814, the once beautiful, sky-blue *New Orleans*, now
somewhat worn and with her paint chipped and sun-faded, impaled herself on a submerged stump near Baton Rouge, and
while she struggled to get off, a great hole was gouged in her
hull. Water rushed in, and the first Mississippi steamboat sank
into the maw of the hungry river. A good many other steamboats were to follow her to this common grave, until the river
bottom literally would be paved with wrecks. The stretch between St. Louis and Cairo possessed so many wrecked boats that
it became known as the "Graveyard." But this came much later.
In the early part of the nineteenth century, the Mississippi, in
spite of steam, was still in actuality a one-way river.

As the city of New Orleans dominated the lower end of the
river, so did the Fulton-Livingston Company dominate the waters
themselves. Only boats owned by the company were permitted
to ply the waters and trade on the Mississippi. Any boats—sail
or steam—from other companies, if any there should happen
to be, which ventured into the forbidden waters of New Orleans
harbor were to have their cargoes confiscated, and were to be

sternly ejected. If they should be so bold as to return after this discouraging reception, boat and all were to be taken, and the owners and captain jailed and fined. The company felt secure in its monopoly of trade for a long time.

The little *Comet*, built by Daniel French and sent down from Pittsburgh, was chased out of New Orleans with threats enough to curl her smokestack. But the *Comet*, even if she had wanted to, couldn't get very far away, couldn't go home. Her laboring engine was unable to take her above Natchez. It was finally removed and put to running a cotton gin. The *Comet* was junked.

But Daniel French built the *Enterprise*, which was a bigger and better boat than the lost *Comet*, with a much more powerful engine. Young Captain Henry M. Shreve, a Quaker, was hired to run the *Enterprise* down to New Orleans and try to get back up the Mississippi, if he could. No one had done so yet, but the calm, convinced Friend, Shreve, thought maybe he would do it. He was going to slip into New Orleans and openly defy the eighteen-year monopoly of the privileges which the Fulton-Livingston Company had wangled from the legislatures of inland river states and territories.

The War of 1812 was approaching its climax as the year 1814 neared its end. It was desperately imperative that Shreve get the *Enterprise* as quickly as possible down to New Orleans with her cargo of ammunition, arms and ordinance, for General Jackson's use in protecting the city. With the aggravating necessity of having to take on wood twice a day, and the need for tying up every night because of the snags, the *Enterprise* nevertheless steamed triumphantly into New Orleans two weeks after she left Pittsburgh.

Shreve found the city on edge with fear, tense with the closeness of the British who were planning an attack. He had arrived opportunely.

"You're just in time, man," exploded harassed General Andy Jackson, beetling his brows at Shreve. "On your way down here, did you see anything of my three keelboats? Started long ago, loaded with small arms—we need 'em bad, and goin' to need 'em worse before this is over. No; didn't see 'em?"

Shreve had indeed seen nothing he had recognized as ammunition boats.

"Then in the name of the United States Government, Captain, I order you to take your steamboat upstream and see if you can find those confounded keels. Light a fire under their tails so they'll skedaddle down here!"

"Right!" said Shreve, grinning.

When he got back to the *Enterprise* at the waterfront, he found the Livingstons of Louisiana waiting to arrest him for daring to enter the city with his boat.

"Bother me later!" he snapped, brushing aside the officers and striding up the plank. "I have business for the Government. This is war, man! Let your silly monopoly wait till we get more important things settled!"

Leaving the Livingston men agape on the docks, Shreve got under way and set off upstream to find the delinquent keelboats. He found them up north of Natchez, dallying along, taking their time, the men stopping at every little landing to trade, oblivious to Jackson's urgent need.

The imposing figure of the indignant Henry Shreve at the bow of the *Enterprise* surprised the keelboatmen.

"Tie your keelboats one to the other," he ordered masters and crew, "and run a line to the stern of the *Enterprise*. That's right. With the current in your favor, you should have been in New Orleans weeks ago. Don't you know there's a war on, and we need your cargo, fast? Now, I'll show you speed!"

It was, perhaps, the first time that a steamboat had ever towed barges or boats on the Mississippi. The *Enterprise* hauled the three keelboats down to New Orleans. He had been gone six and one-half days, round trip, and had traveled 654 miles. Men in New Orleans, when they heard of this record trip, could hardly believe the truth of it. The freedom of this steamboat, the speed . . .

The war was drawing uncomfortably close. Shreve used the *Enterprise* to carry men, supplies and arms down to Chalmette plantation, where a battle was shaping up, and was able to run upstream again. Several other craft had not been so lucky. Out on the river were two armed American schooners, the *Carolina* and the *Louisiana* The British were camped in the swamps downstream a little way, so when night fell, the *Carolina* slipped quietly down the Mississippi to fire into the enemy camp. The British, though caught momentarily off guard when grapeshot began to be tossed into their midst, fired back and bombarded the *Carolina* unmercifully. Finally, a shot hit the powder and the ship scattered herself all over the river and the swamp.

Jackson, undiscouraged, sent the *Louisiana* down next. While pieces of the *Carolina* were still floating seaward on the river, the sister ship tossed in more shells. However, when the crew wanted to sail back upriver, to get out of range of the bombardment which promptly followed this cordial salute, there was no wind, the Mississippi current was against them, and for a little bit things looked ticklish in the extreme.

Then the captain ordered out the small boats. Strong lines were tied to them, and to the ship. Whereupon, the men desperately rowed for their lives up the river, towing the big ship behind, stern first, until she got out of firing range of the British.

Shreve, meanwhile, was using the *Enterprise* to carry women and children from threatened New Orleans fifty miles upstream to a haven of safety. Jackson wished he had a dozen *Enterprises* to fight his war on the Mississippi. After the experiences of the *Carolina* and the *Louisiana*, he could see that sails were not especially useful or efficient on a river like the Mississippi.

General Jackson, however, had no time to waste in wishing for what he didn't have He had a war on his hands, a battle in his front yard and a motley collection of fighting men, which included rough, tough backwoodsmen with Kentucky rifles and deadly aim, who were stationed on big log rafts out among the cypresses, where they spent a good deal of time in picking off the

British, one by one. He had excitable Creoles and Hinds' Dragoons in full uniform, and he had the pirates.

They were Jean Lafitte's gang from Grand Isle, out in the swamps of the Barataria Country, along the gulf. Pirates, murderers and thieves, they knew the swamps as they knew the palms of their hands. Lafitte had gone to General Jackson to offer the services of his Barataria men.

"If you will permit my brother, Pierre, to go free, whom you hold prisoner for no reason at all, I will bring all my men and we will win this battle for you. Me, Lafitte—I will win it single-handed!"

The cold Jackson eyes bored into the insolent black ones. Those frigid eyes could freeze the marrow in lesser men's bones, but Jean Lafitte did not freeze easily.

"I am not to be bought," Jackson said, and turned back to his paper.

But somehow, one day soon afterward, there was swarthy Pierre Lafitte out of jail and a free man again. The pirates at Grand Isle and along the bayous and hidden islands in the Mississippi delta, gathering up their assorted firearms and weapons, came in their fast, slim pirogues through bayou and canal and river, to New Orleans. In the distance could be heard the noise of guns.

Whether or not the pirates won the Battle of New Orleans, or even helped turn it the right way, no one knows. Certain it is that Henry Shreve and the *Enterprise* had a good deal to do with it, and so did those Kentucky rifles out in the swamps. On January 8, the Battle of New Orleans broke forth along the long-suffering river, and was over in three hours. It was over, and the war was finished.

Shreve was anxious to hurry back up the Mississippi with the busy *Enterprise*—he had been away too long from his family—but government errands kept him in the South. On May 6, as Shreve was about to leave at last for Louisville, the Livingston

Company boarded the *Enterprise* and took it over.

Shreve had been expecting this. His lawyer was ready. Bail was promptly posted and the captain departed.

"Oh, let him go," the Livingston men sneered, watching the sidewheels of the *Enterprise* smacking the water. "He'll not get far, and when he has to turn around and come back here, like a whipped cur, then we'll take over, and with no trouble."

"You're right," someone else agreed. "No steamboat has ever yet managed to get back up the river, not beyond Baton Rouge, anyway. Louisville! Ha! *He'll* never make it!"

The river was rising. It was spreading all through the bottom-land plantations, so that the force of the current was less than if the river ran lower within its defined banks. To take advantage of slack water whenever possible, Shreve ran the *Enterprise* boldly through flooded lowlands, avoiding trees, somehow man-handling his boat and its laboring engine through vicious eddies and boils, all the way upriver.

And he made it. The first round trip for a steamboat was his personal record. Henry Shreve reached Louisville on the last day of May, 1815. It had taken nearly four years for a steamboat to accomplish a return up the river. Shreve had spent fifty-four days in traveling 2,200 miles, twenty days of which were spent in loading or unloading passengers and cargo along the way. People were amazed, were awed. Here indeed was a double record.

Shreve accepted the praise, but he knew that without slack water and flood, his steamboat might still be floundering around near Baton Rouge. He could see the faults in the *Enterprise*, which made it so weak against a heavy current, but he couldn't persuade the builder, Daniel French, of those faults, nor of the necessity for a shallower draft. In impatience, Shreve stopped trying to convince anyone of what was needed. He simply set out to build a boat for himself.

And so the steamboat *Washington* was built. The keel was laid September 10, 1815, at Wheeling, West Virginia But it was not a keel like those that other boats had. It was barely a suggestion of one. Shreve made the hull out of weathered timbers taken from old Fort Henry. The finished boat was very shallow of draft, but it had two decks, stacked one on the other like a layer cake. There were rooms for passengers, not in the hold but on deck. It had twin engines which people shook their heads over, sagely: those engines would never propel a 150-foot boat. Never! When Shreve put the engines on the lower deck and the four boilers on the upper deck, and had the cylinders installed horizontally, as the boilers were, it looked more and more impossible.

But the machinery was strategically located for balance. It had a fraction of the weight of Fulton's machinery, but was many times more powerful.

June 4, 1816, and the steamboat *Washington*, built on an entirely new plan, which was to become the standard design of almost all Mississippi steamboats in the future, left for New Orleans. Everyone knew what was going to happen when Shreve got there. The Monopoly was waiting for him!

But while the new vessel was still in the Ohio, going well below Marietta, she suddenly got out of hand, headed toward shore, and a boiler blew up.

Even so dreadful a calamity did not daunt Henry Shreve. When he had recovered from his steam burns from the accident, he repaired the damaged parts, and again the *Washington* set off for her personal Battle of New Orleans.

Promptly, on her arrival, the Fulton-Livingston Company ordered the boat seized and held for ten thousand dollars' bail. But when Shreve's canny lawyer said that, in that event, the Company must put up like bail, not to be returned to them if Shreve won the case, the suit was suddenly dropped. Shreve deposited his cargo, picked up more, and with an enthusiastic load of passengers, he returned to Louisville. The sturdy *Washington* climbed the river easily.

When spring released the waters for travel again, back he came. You couldn't keep Shreve from something that he wanted to do. Again he was arrested and released on a technicality.

Next trip, the company offered Henry Shreve a part interest in the Fulton-Livingston Steamboat Company, if he would give up his idea of ending its monopoly and freeing the river to trade.

It was tempting. But Henry Shreve was too deeply dedicated to his crusade of improving and freeing the river to consider the offer. Although it would have fattened his lean purse, it dreadfully insulted his inner honesty.

Shreve, in a huff, sailed back to Louisville with a full list of passengers, eager to ride on the beautiful two-way boat. It was a luxury cruise like nothing ever known before on the Mississippi or the Ohio. He carried, besides the passengers, fifty-five tons of freight. After ten days in Louisville, he started back for New Orleans and the usual bout with the Livingstons.

When the *Washington* chuffed, bells ringing, up to the New Orleans wharf, people came running, alarmed at seeing her so soon.

Shreve laughed at their concern. He had simply gone up to Louisville, discharged his load, picked up another, and here he was. He had traveled, heavily loaded, in a little more than three weeks from New Orleans to Louisville. At this incredible news, the people went wild . . . especially those who were concerned with shipping goods about the country. With speed like this, with boats like this, the whole of inland America would be closely adjacent to New Orleans, New York, St. Louis, Louisville, Pittsburgh and the ports of the world. Not only that, but the battle of the Monopoly was finally over. Shreve's persistent passive resistance and his appeals to the United States Supreme Court had won. The Court had decreed freedom of the rivers.

It was 1819. The river was a great highway ready for the Steamboat Era, which burgeoned in the years ahead with grander and more luxuriant steamboats, huge steamboats, dangerous steamboats, steamboats with elaborate menus and sumptuous accommodations for cabin passengers.

Lying athwart the Mississippi, however, was one more great obstacle to successful transportation on that vast highway. This was the snags, the millions of snags, remains of trees long ago fallen in and carried on the waters until they dropped and rooted themselves securely, their great, murderous lances poised to gouge the heart out of a passing steamboat. Losses from snags amounted to millions of dollars. And so the man who solved the problem of one-way steamboats on a two-way river, the man who licked the Monopoly, conquered the snags.

Henry Shreve invented the snagboat. After a long battle for support and to finance his curious craft, he was commissioned by the U.S. Corps of Engineers to take his twin-hulled boat, the *Heliopolis*, to the Ohio and Mississippi, to remove the forests of snags.

He cut out, sawed into short lengths and sent floating as harmless logs all the terrible imbedded lances which made Plum Point Reach the most snag-infested area on the river. He routed out the "sleepers," those submerged snags, from their most abundant area near Helena, Arkansas, as well as all up and down the Mississippi. He destroyed thousands of "sawyers," those snags which rock on the current. The *Heliopolis* was the marvel of the Mississippi; other boats gathered around while the crews watched how the *Heliopolis* rammed head-on into ponderous sunken trees which would have wrecked a lesser craft, and conquered them utterly.

In a few months Henry Shreve had cleared the river of snags. At the same time, he had cleared the way for the Steamboat Era to advance with its hundreds of beautiful, ornate, smoking, splashing vessels, all patterned basically on that first successful two-way boat, the little *Washington*.

CHAPTER ELEVEN

1842: *"The earth is satisfied with the fruit of thy work."*
BOOK OF PSALMS

THE tall young girl stood before her father in his office, situated close to the big, brick sugar house on the plantation. Her full, flowered gown seemed to fill half the room. Out beyond the azalea gardens, beyond the royal palms and the big oaks, beyond the levee, she could see the Mississippi sparkling as it flowed past. A steamboat, she could halfway discover, was nosing upstream, sternwheel churning white water. Another boat, grand as a huge white wedding cake, had just passed, and the little Negro boys fishing at the landing had grinned and waved. A field hand with a hoe on his shoulder rounded a corner of the big d'Estrehan mansion.

The girl brought her attention back to the stout man in the

big chair. His left hand rested on a battered mahogany desk. But no hand at all thrust from the right sleeve of his ruffled white shirt.

Now he spoke.

"Louie," said Nicholas Noel d'Estrehan fondly, admiring for the thousandth time how self-possessed this tall daughter of his was, and how lovely to look at, with her serious brown eyes and well-brushed curls pulled back with a blue ribbon. What a pity her mother had not lived to see her daughter grow up so well!

"Louie," he went on, "it is time you made something of yourself. Of my four children, you, *cheri*, and you only, have any brains worth mentioning. Azby is all right in his way, and so are Eliza and Adele, but they haven't what it takes to understand business, nor ever will.

"Now you, Louie, *ma petite*, you have sense!"

"But, Papa, what do you mean?" cried Louise d'Estrehan, half frightened at the excited, intense expression on her father's florid face.

"This is what I mean!" Nicholas Noel exclaimed, banging his left hand on the desk so that the inkwell jumped. "I am turning over to you—to you only, Louise—the business accounts of the d'Estrehan Canal. I have too much to do with the sugar business to handle anything more. You will learn to manage the entire business of the waterway. It is carrying much traffic now, from New Orleans to Baratana and beyond, and brings in a great deal of revenue."

"Oh, but, Papa, I couldn't!" cried fourteen-year-old Louise.

"I will teach you," he said implacably. "You have a brilliant mind, Daughter. It won't take you long to learn. It's a pity to let you dally your time away with fripperies like music and painting and embroidery!"

But it was simply unheard of in Louisiana, at that period in history, for a woman—a girl—to know anything about business, much less to have it turned over to her by her rich if eccentric father! Girls on the plantations were reared gently, taught ladylike pursuits, instructed lightly in the basic essentials of reading, writing and enough arithmetic to keep household accounts fairly straight. They were taught painting and music, manners, morals and how to flirt in a ladylike way. They were expected to marry young and rear their own daughters in the same fashion.

Nicholas Noel d'Estrehan, in flying in the face of precedence and custom, knew what he was doing. His daughter was indeed brilliant, while his son was gay and bent only on pleasure and spending his father's money. Nicholas Noel pulled his daughter down to his knee and kissed her resoundingly. The arm without a hand held her close for a moment, then released her. It was Louise d'Estrehan's last day as a child. Thereafter she was a woman, with great responsibilities and no time for fun.

It was back in 1720 when the first d'Estrehan, named Jean Baptiste d'Estrehan des Tours, Royal Treasurer, came from France to take up a large land grant immediately south and west of the Mississippi, below New Orleans. It was a wild, impossible country, in which no roads could be built because of the ground water and the ever present cypress swamps.

But instead of retreating to France, Jean Baptiste sent men out into the desolate swampland to dig a canal to drain it. With spades and axes—small, futile, Old World tools—they gouged and cut a clear-water road through desperate cypress jungles and open cane marshes which lay unending to the horizon and the Gulf of Mexico.

The d'Estrehan slaves labored in the heat. Some slipped in and drowned in the black and muddy waters. Others were maimed by alligators, or died in the enervating Louisiana heat. Since a man's Negro slaves cost money, it is doubtful if these were of that sort. They were more likely to have been indentured white men or captured Natchez Indians, whose lives would cost their owner nothing!

At any rate, at whatever human cost, there appeared soon after 1720 a canal extending five miles southwestward from the

Mississippi River to Bayou Barataria. Thus the river was connected with the Gulf of Mexico more directly than one might travel by way of the Passes and the mouth. And, although the canal was intended primarily as drainage, it was from the beginning taken over by water transportation. Later widened to take bigger boats, the d'Estrehan Canal became known as the best route to the vast southwestern wilderness of Louisiana and Texas, and from that day to this it has been in constant use.

Shortly after that first d'Estrehan came to Louisiana and cut a canal, a certain Asiatic crop was being planted in that southern country along the Mississippi. Colonists were taking up large plantation acreages, beginning to create the plantation autocracy which reached its peak just before the War between the States. It was a world which was based on the cheap labor of Negro slaves and on the rich Mississippi earth and the long growing season. From this triumvirate, planters began to wrest fortunes from the Mississippi country.

At first, what to plant was a problem, since Louisiana and the Mississippi were quite unlike France and the Seine. In the strange land and extremely rich earth, and in an unpredictable climate, the settlers had to experiment with crops which would be profitable and successful.

In the interior of Louisiana one year, an observing French priest discovered wild indigo. He recognized it as related to the indigo which for many years had been imported from India to supply the dye needs of France and its great cloth manufactories. Soon men were planting wild indigo in Louisiana. Processed, the American species produced a moderately good blue color. Later, however, the even better Asiatic indigo was imported from India. The business grew and became the chief export crop of the planters along the Mississippi, with the d'Estrehans among the top producers. They blessed the indigo for their new-found wealth.

Then suddenly, in the summer of 1793, slaves ran to tell the overseers of the calamity. Caterpillars were devouring the indigo

plants, were eating the blue-stained stalks down to the ground
The crop was ruined! Caterpillars wrecked it the next year, and
the next, until in desperation the planters saw their earlier profits
vanishing, and no income from their ravaged fields.

Far back in the days of Bienville, a small amount of West
Indian sugar cane had been planted near New Orleans. Perhaps
some of the sad-eyed slaves from Santo Domingo secretly had
brought it along. The roots grew easily in the humid climate and
the ever-damp black earth near the Mississippi. By 1750, both
sugar cane and the Barbadoes Negroes who were skilled in its
cultivation were brought to Louisiana. In all the years, however,
in which it was grown and used for the molasses and rum which
were produced from its crushed stems and juice, no one could
perfect a method of granulating American sugar. It was only a
thick, dark, sweet, granular syrup, called milk sugar, none of that
white loaf sugar which was so much to be desired and which
would bring high prices.

When the indigo crop was in its third year of failure in the
broad, black fields along the Mississippi—when acre after acre
showed only rows of stark, blue-stained, pale stalks, well stripped
of all their leaves, and the caterpillars were crawling about hunting for more—things looked hopeless on many a plantation in
Louisiana.

Jean Noel d'Estrehan, descendant of that first d'Estrehan, sat
in his West Indian-style plantation house, on the east bank of
the Mississippi. The River Road connected him and his fields
with the houses and fields of other planters, up to Baton Rouge
and down to New Orleans, with the river connecting all by
means of steamboats which made more than a thousand stops
in that distance. Jean Noel d'Estrehan contemplated his pistol
lying on the polished mahogany desk which had come from
Martinique. Whether to use the pistol now, and get it over with,
end this worry and failure and disgrace, or hold out a little longer,
just a little longer. A cotton crop next year instead of the ill-fated

indigo might help to recoup his fortunes, would save honor and
life. His slender fingers caressed the shining barrel. It would take
so little to finish it all. Now.

But Jean Noel d'Estrehan waited. In the spring he planted
cotton. And on a chill, damp autumn day in the year 1795, the
d'Estrehan slaves were bending over the cotton rows Dozens of
men, women and children were dragging their sacks and stuffing
them with the fluffy bolls. The slaves sang mournful African
chants as they walked; some sang religious songs which contained
in themselves some of the primitive African motif, dirges sung
for a lost heritage, a lost freedom. Jean Noel, watching from the
veranda across which blew mists from the river, wondered how
good the crop would be.

A horseman came pounding down the River Road.

"Papa, Papa," cried little Nicholas Noel d'Estrehan, running
on his short, fat legs from the gate to the house under the great
oaks with their dripping moss. "Look, we have company!"

The small, slight figure on the horse got down stiffly and
turned over his mount to the Negro boy who had hurried up.
The visitor walked with a limp along the oyster-shell path and
met Jean Noel d'Estrehan standing on the veranda. The two
clasped hands.

"Welcome, Etienne, my good friend," cried Jean Noel, leading his guest inside and seating him on a satin upholstered chair.
A Negro girl came in with coffee, for the day was cold.

"Now tell me what has brought you here," went on d'Estrehan, seating himself and sipping the black, strong, Louisiana
brew.

"It is just this, my friend," began Etienne de Boré, his black
eyes snapping sparks. "I have found a way to granulate sugar so
that it comes white every time! White and pure and crystalline!
And I can do it in quantity and in a hurry. Jean, we are made!
Plant sugar cane in all your fields, buy more land; plant all the
cane you can obtain. Send to the Indies now, this very day, by
the next ship, and order all the slips of cane you can buy, be-

cause we have found the way to make sugar profitable along the Mississippi! We will supply all of America and France with sugar! Sugar, Jean! White and clean and pure, no more of that miserable brown stuff, no sand in it, no discoloration!"

"How do you know all this?" cried Jean d'Estrehan, rising and holding on to the back of his chair. His knuckles whitened.

"I have done it—I, myself, and so I know," went on Etienne de Boré in poorly concealed pride.

The secret of making sugar granulate had been used to produce very small amounts, always unreliable, by a long and tedious process, in private sugar mills on the plantations.

"I have found the way, Jean. Only last week I sold my entire crop for $12,000.00! Imagine! And I could have sold five times the amount at that figure! People are mad for white sugar."

That was what Jean Noel d'Estrehan and the other nearly ruined indigo planters were looking for. Cotton was profitable, but sugar would be even more so. As for indigo—it was suddenly a forgotten, discarded crop. Let the caterpillars have it. In the d'Estrehan fields and all along the River Road and beyond the river to the west, the tall, waving, green sugar cane, like the huge grass that it was, bent in winds off the gulf. In the autumn, the great stalks were cut and brought to the mill. The cane was sent through big rollers, to take out the sweet juice, was cooked in the evaporating pans, was treated with lime and filtered, the molasses drained off, the crude brown sugar treated again so that it recrystallized like magic into sparkling white granules It could be done in the small mills, or else the crop could be sent by cart or steamboat down to the big refinery at New Orleans which had been operating by de Boré's method since 1802. Men grew rich from waving green fields of cane.

So also did Jean Noel d'Estrehan. He built a new mansion, a grand house under the oaks, also constructed in the West Indian style with broad eaves. As his family grew, and there were finally fourteen children, he added wings to the main body of the house. The oaks grew, and the moss waved in the river wind. Life was very pleasant and a little bit unreal on the plantation, as it was on so many of the plantations arranged along either side of the Mississippi. *Belmont, Bon Secours, Glendale* and *Belle Grove* . . . *Germania, Uncle Sam, Evergreen* and *Palo Alto* . . . *Point Clair, Belle Helene, Soulouque* and *Longwood* . . . these and many more margined the Mississippi with a world of their own creating.

It was a world in which the lord of the manor and his overseers governed and cared for the dozens of slaves who lived in their own small brick houses, back by the big sugar house. It was they who worked the fields of corn and cotton and sugar, who harvested the crops, who made the sugar, who kept the great mansion clean and who cared for the fourteen children under the d'Estrehan roof. The slaves loaded cotton bales and sugar sacks when the steamboat came up to the little levee which was all that kept the river out of the d'Estrehan front yard.

"Papa," once said young Nicholas Noel d'Estrehan when he was growing up, "what would we do without the slaves to work for us?"

Jean Noel d'Estrehan turned fiercely upon his son.

"Never mention it, my son!" he snapped. "Without the slaves we would be ruined! Ruined!"

When Nicholas Noel d'Estrehan grew to manhood, he took over the management of his father's sugar mill. It was here one day that he lost his right hand. His coat was caught in the cane crusher, drawing his hand and wrist in, pulling him farther and farther within the terrible jaws of the crusher. Nicholas Noel yelled at the nearest slave:

"The cane knife—cut off my hand! Quick! Quick!"

And it was done. Bleeding terribly, he was helped to the house by one of the slaves, whose lips were gray with horror. For a long while no one felt they could stop the flow of blood, nor save young Nicholas Noel's fast waning life. But at last the doctor arrived, galloping furiously down the River Road with a black boy leading the way through the night. Young Nick's life was saved. He learned to manage very well with his left hand.

And the years moved pleasantly along under the d'Estrehan oaks. The mockingbirds sang and the slaves sang, and steamboats whistled mellowly from the Mississippi.

Nicholas Noel married a beautiful girl from New Orleans and built her a splendid mansion down near the canal, which was still in the family, a profitable business. The great house was an elaborate castle, but before she could live in it or appreciate its art treasures, Madame d'Estrehan died. In grief, Nicholas Noel closed the house forever. Some years later, it burned to the ground.

And so it was that when Nicholas Noel d'Estrehan's daughter Louise was in her early teens, her father called her into his office. Before him was the same desk, now battered and marred, on which had lain his father's pistol.

Louise d'Estrehan learned the canal business. When she was sixteen, there came her father's next command: marry Captain Joseph Hale Harvey. He was considerably older than the child-woman who knew so much about canals and ledgers and river traffic, and so little about life itself.

Three years later, Nicholas Noel died. The slave regime had come to an end. The slaves were free. A planter had to pay them to work the fields. The d'Estrehans might have been ruined if they had not had the canal business for revenue At Nicholas Noel's death, the canal passed into the hands of the Harveys, as he had planned, and was called the Harvey Canal, which is probably what old Nicholas Noel hadn't exactly bargained for. The captain, besides, had his own ideas about woman's place in the world, so he decided to take over the canal business himself. Eight years later, he had the canal greatly deepened and enlarged to take care of the heavier traffic and bigger boats from the Mississippi. In 1880, the captain started the construction of locks, but they were never completed, though a lock gate, which was used only when the waterway and the river were at the same level, finally came into use in 1909.

Long before 1909, however, Captain Harvey died.

"Poor Louise Harvey," people said when they heard of it. "What will she do now? Such a gentlewoman, in spite of that father of hers making her go into business like a man. Fancy! But poor, dear Louise—she is a woman rare in this world. They say she has never raised her voice in anger to a child, and has always worn silk!"

Louise d'Estrehan Harvey found herself the surviving parent of nine children and owner of a huge and costly home, built for her by the expansive captain, which had become a landmark on the Mississippi. She owned the canal business which the sometimes improvident Captain Harvey had permitted to run considerably into debt while she, at home, fumed at his ineptness and supervised the children.

People on the lower Mississippi called her Queen Louise. Descendant of the first determined d'Estrehan who had cut a canal in the swamps, she had known only wealth, ease and the sugar business, had taken on a canal and a husband when she was still a child. So she went back to managing the canal. The business grew, and Queen Louise was in her element again. And the years unaccountably sped by. In 1904, when repairs and improvements were underway, she scrambled briskly up and down ladders and over narrow catwalks and knew all that was going on. In vain, did her children remind her that she was seventy-six and ought to take things easier But at last the day came when Louise d'Estrehan Harvey, the grand old lady of the Mississippi, did not rise from her bed, and with her going an era connected far in the past had ended. She had been a living link with the old days long dead along the river. Even before her own departure, many of the old plantation houses along the river road had fallen into ruins and so had the way of life they had fostered.

When plans for the Gulf Intracoastal Waterway were being formed, they included taking over the old d'Estrehan-Harvey

Canal. In 1924, the Harvey grandchildren received $425,000 for the old ditch dug by Great-great-great-great-grandpa's slaves, and Grandpa's little lock gate which was so seldom used. Great locks and gates were built. Various bayous and rivers were connected with the existing canal by dredging, so that the Gulf Intracoastal Waterway eventually stretched from New Orleans and the Mississippi's shores to Port Arthur, Texas, a distance of 285 miles.

And so it came about that a canal, a waterway, a crop which was eaten by caterpillars, Etienne de Boré and his sugar mill, the d'Estrehans and their mansion, the plantation aristocracy along the River Road and the steamboats connecting them with a thread of communication are all woven into one story, inseparable from the story of the Mississippi.

CHAPTER TWELVE

1832: *"For the day of their calamity is at hand,
and their doom comes swiftly."*
DEUTERONOMY, 32

IN the Sac tribe, at the mouth of the Rock River in northern
Illinois, two powers had contested for years—the power of the
war-maker, Black Hawk, and the power of the peace-maker,
Keokuk Keokuk's broad, intelligent, understanding features were
as different from Black Hawk's thin, sharply discontented, selfish
ones as the two Indians were different from each other.

Black Hawk was a British Indian who did his share in harrying
settlers during the American Revolution. Afterward, he received
annual presents from the British for his services. This was pleasant enough to Black Hawk, who could not, however, see why

he should cease his private warfare against the whites, just because the British themselves had given up on the Americans. It was irksome to him to observe the Sacs signing treaty after treaty which gave them money for their lands, annual gifts in a great amount and the protection of American soldiers, in case other tribes attacked, when he himself had never ceased to hate the Americans and was still in the pay of the British.

Consequently, in retaliation for fancied wrongs, or simply for his love of injuring the hated Americans, Black Hawk over the years, between the end of the American Revolution and the year 1828, had attacked and harried. He had murdered Indians of other tribes, had instigated the attack on Fort Madison, on the Mississippi, and had wanted to go down to attack St. Louis, during the War of 1812.

When the fertile land around the mouth of the Rock River, which the Sacs, years before, had sold to the Americans, was being taken up by settlers, Black Hawk was more furious than ever. Keokuk, however, who may have seen it coming, agreed when the President of the United States requested him to move with his people across the Mississippi and set up a new town on the pleasant Iowa River. Keokuk and Pash-e-pa-ho obediently went with the Sacs, and with them went Wapello, Chief of the Foxes, with his people, but Black Hawk and Quash-qua-me and the war band of Sacs did not go.

Black Hawk was surly. The Americans were ousting him from his lands. It was not fair, the Americans were never fair. He would fight them to the death. Repeatedly, Keokuk and Wapello anxiously reminded him of the treaties they had signed, of the annuities they had been receiving for many years, promptly and to the full amount always, to provide comforts for their people, in payment for the land which now the white men wanted. There were lots of other places for Indians to live. It was just as good across the river, and he should come with them and cause no more trouble, to ruin the good name of the Sacs and Foxes. But Black Hawk would not go.

By May, 1828, when all the Sacs and Foxes had gone, excepting the stubborn war band, Black Hawk discovered how he could annoy his white neighbors. Indian horses often broke down the fences of the white farmers and trampled and ate their corn and grain, so Black Hawk saw to it that many more horses were driven into the fields, to cause even more damage. Often he sniped at the livestock of the farmers; he and his young men burned hay ricks, sometimes pulled down a barn or a house. When settlers protested to Black Hawk in person, he drew back his thin lips in a sneer.

"You should be glad the damages are so little," he said proudly, looking down his beaklike nose at the angry and worried farmers. "For if I am sufficiently annoyed, I may burn down your house while you sleep. . . . I and my young men may become so angry that we will go on the war path and scalp you and your women and children. So be thankful it is only your miserable corn and beans!"

The alarmed farmers wrote to the Governor of Illinois. When no attention was paid to their pleas for help, the farmers continued sending letters until Governor Reynolds awoke to the fact that Indian trouble was not a thing of the past, but was taking place in his own territory, in the civilized State of Illinois. Governor Reynolds called up the militia.

"In order to protect the citizens of this State, who reside near Rock River, from Indian invasion and depredation, I have considered it necessary to call out a force of militia of this State of about seven hundred strong, to remove a band of Sac Indians who are now about Rock Island . . . peaceably, if they can, but forcibly if they must. Those Indians are now, and so I have considered them, in a state of actual invasion of the State."

Meanwhile, scenting trouble and enjoying the prospect of it at last, Black Hawk politically invited the Potawatomis and Winnebagoes to join him in war. He felt he could use reinforcements.

"Who is Black Hawk?" he declared arrogantly. "Provoke our people to war, and all will learn who Black Hawk is!"

Governor Reynolds asked for 700 men from counties north of St. Clair and west of Sangamon. Almost twice that number left their plows and their work and gathered at Beardstown, on the Illinois River, about 160 miles south and east of Black Hawk and his country. Poorly equipped and armed, it took the assorted militia, 1,600 strong, already chafing at having to take orders, some days to march north to Fort Armstrong and the Indians. A steamboat set off up the Mississippi at the same time, to bring the supplies.

Where the Rock River flows into the Mississippi, the terrain was difficult. The army found both streams deep and unfordable. Within sight of the Indian village on the hill opposite them, they had to waste time while scows were brought to bring them over within gun range. Meanwhile, the men lived in momentary fear of attack. Indians hidden in the underbrush of the river bottoms and the islands, or in the village itself, could have picked them off one by one.

But nothing happened. The lack of anything happening was almost worse than attack itself. At least they would have known what to do, and here they were doing nothing, uneasily waiting.

Makeshift scows were hastily knocked together, to ferry soldiers and guns across. When at last, with exhausting effort, the militia, guns ready for action, climbed the hill to confront the errant Black Hawk, they found the village quite empty and silent. Before daylight, the Sacs had paddled quietly across the Mississippi to the Iowa shore and avoided a battle neatly and conclusively.

The soldiers were furious. They were humiliated to find nothing at the end of such a hard march, when they had been led to believe they would find fighting Indians. The men therefore set about wreaking their vengeance on anything at hand, which included burning the Sac village. While they were about it, a storm came up. Rain descended in torrents which put out the flaming houses, but they were too badly ruined for the men to find shelter in any of them, which only made them more angry.

The damp, muddy, frustrated army marched down to Fort Armstrong for several days and camped there, while General Gaines called a peace parley. He demanded Black Hawk's presence. Black Hawk insolently sent a group of his braves instead. He refused to budge until General Gaines, with threats, insisted that he come. So Black Hawk came, sullen and superior and sneering.

In June, 1831, another treaty was signed on the banks of the Mississippi, saying, among other items which had been said in the other treaties and had been blandly disregarded, that "the British band of Sacs should thereafter live and hunt on the west side of the Mississippi and leave the settlers strictly alone." On this document Black Hawk and twenty-seven braves of the Sac and Fox made their marks—ranging from Pash-e-pa-ho, the Stabbing Chief, at the head of the list, down to Ka-ke-me-ka-peo, Sitting in the Grease.

But a treaty meant nothing at all to Black Hawk. Soon he was at it again, this time killing Sioux and Menominees west of the Mississippi, and getting into trouble generally. Keokuk, in a long and splendid speech, tried to help matters. He was tired of being blamed for all the faults of the Sacs—and of Black Hawk —just because he, Keokuk, was their chief.

"I expect it is because our names are Sacs and Foxes that you make a noise about it," he said wearily to the white officers. "When we do the least thing, you make a great noise about it. Last winter I went to the Missouri. There an Ioway killed an Omaha. Why was he not hung? They were at the treaty. The reason I say so much against you is because our hearts are good. As for my chiefs and braves, they will do as they please . . . why do you not let us fight? Your whites are constantly fighting. Why do you not interfere with them? Why do you not let us be as the Great Spirit made us, and let us settle our difficulties?"

Meanwhile, as Keokuk was desperately trying to keep peace, Black Hawk was busily sending out runners to many points.

Some went as far away as the Gulf of Mexico, in an effort to gather around Black Hawk the confederacy of tribes which Tecumseh had attempted in the War of 1812, but in which he had failed. Black Hawk failed, too, though his runners returned with tales that an immense force of Indians from down the Mississippi Valley would rally around him when the time came to strike at the white man the great blow he contemplated.

Enormously encouraged by this, Black Hawk sent his lieutenant, Nea-pope, to Canada, to try for aid from the British. Nea-pope had little luck in that corner and came back somewhat disconsolate and not relishing the prospect of facing Black Hawk's wrath. On his return, he stopped at the village of Wabo-kie-shiek, the Winnebago Prophet who lived about forty miles from the mouth of the Rock River and Black Hawk's domain. The Prophet was a malignant, vicious individual who loved to make trouble for the whites, so long as he himself didn't get involved openly in it. He saw a beautiful opportunity for this when he heard Nea-pope's tale of Black Hawk's wide-spread plans.

"A vision—a vision comes before my eyes . . . be silent while the spirit speaks!" muttered Wabo-kie-shiek, suddenly rolling his eyes back into his head and jerking his body convulsively. Nea-pope froze, watching in awe.

The Prophet quivered and jerked and muttered. When he emerged from his trance, he spoke.

"The Black Hawk will take up the hatchet again against the detestable whites," proclaimed the Prophet to the amazed Nea-pope. "He will be joined by the Great Spirit and a great army of Indians. The whites will be vanquished—I speak it truly—and the Sacs and Foxes will be restored to their ancient villages in the land of their ancestors. I have spoken. It is so!" The Prophet was finished. He observed the gullible Nea-pope narrowly.

Nea-pope, in wonderment and delight, rushed back to Black Hawk and told about the vision which the Prophet had had, while Wabo-kie-shiek sat in his own house and rocked with evil laughter Black Hawk, he knew, would take it all so seriously.

There was no knowing how much trouble he would make for the whites before they finally vanquished him—before retribution, swift and terrible, wiped out Black Hawk and his band.

Black Hawk's campaign began by urging his people to steal food from the settlers. All winter and all spring, the raids increased. Black Hawk, meanwhile, sent some of his men into Keokuk's village in Iowa, to undermine his peaceful disposition and to corrupt the people under him so that they would turn to Black Hawk. Then he marched with his entire force of braves to Keokuk's village, to dispute his supremacy.

"I shall find out once and for all who is chief—who is worthy of being chief!" Black Hawk shouted. "What has this milky-mouthed Keokuk done for the honor of the Sacs? Nothing! We shall see who is chief now!"

It was a touchy moment. As Black Hawk harangued Keokuk's disturbed people, he could see them turning, half unwillingly, half gladly, to the life of war he was urging upon them. Keokuk, watching, almost felt his own heart turning back to savagery. Yet he was still wise enough to know that, if he followed the warring Black Hawk, then all the Sacs and Foxes would join. The other tribes of the north, along the Mississippi and eastward to Lake Michigan, would likely come in, too, so that no farm and white man would be safe along the Great River and in all that northern land. He knew, also, that the white men were strong enough to call up so large an army that no Indian would afterward remain alive.

Keokuk held himself in check. He let Black Hawk talk, let him shout until his thin face was dark and dripped with perspiration, waited until he had finished at last.

Then Keokuk rose. He spoke to the assembled braves, who had been stirred to a heated pitch of excitement by Black Hawk's words.

"Yes," said Keokuk with fine scorn, watching his people. "Yes. Go and fight the whites. You are right. It is fitting that we do so.

But first, before you take leave of this place, you must kill all our old men and our squaws and our children," he warned, significantly, slowly and solemnly, then added, with deep emotion, "for *you will never come back to see them again!*"

Suddenly, as if he had poured water over them, the fire left the braves.

"You have been imposed upon by liars!" Keokuk went on sturdily, ignoring Black Hawk's glare.

And when he had finished, Black Hawk and his war band knew that they had no supporters here. They departed to make war on the whites without the help of Keokuk and his people.

April 6, 1832. Black Hawk, against orders from the United States Government, crossed to the east bank of the Mississippi. With him were between four hundred and five hundred horsemen; other braves came in canoes, so his whole band, including the women and children of the warriors, brought the total to about two thousand people. When anyone asked him, Black Hawk said righteously that he and his people were going to join their friends, the Winnebagoes, to make a crop of corn, because the land in Iowa was poor and fit for nothing.

"FELLOW CITIZENS:" came an order to the militia of the northwestern section of the State of Illinois:

"Your country requires your services. The Indians have assumed a hostile attitude and have invaded the State in violation of the treaty of last summer. The British band of Sacs and other hostile Indians, headed by Black Hawk, are in possession of the Rock River country, to the great terror of the frontier inhabitants. I consider the settlers on the frontiers to be in imminent danger . . ."

The militia was besieged by April rain and deep mud. With young Abraham Lincoln as a captain in the Fourth Regiment, the soldiers moved again to Rock River. Lincoln had been chosen for this post by a popular vote of the men, but almost at once he ran into difficulties in his newly vested authority. The freshly mustered soldiers were fiercely independent individuals who were of a mind to take orders from no man.

"Company, fall in!" shouted Captain Lincoln.

"Go to the devil!" his men snapped back at him.

Under Major Isaiah Stillman, about two hundred men left the rest of the militia and the bulk of the baggage and supplies and, with rations for only three days, pushed on in an erratic and wild pursuit of the Indians. The men could hardly be restrained in their eagerness to get at the savages. That was what they had come for, what they had left their work and plows for, and they weren't going home, like that militia last year, without a single shot being fired. To make sure of that, the reckless recruits went about firing off their guns until they were warned by furious Colonel Dodge to quit. Most of them did, being urged by the blaze in the colonel's eyes at this flagrant breech of army discipline.

Under Stillman, they camped near Old Man's Creek, and the rain poured. That evening, three Indians from Black Hawk's band approached cautiously with a white flag. Back on the hill, five Sacs sat on their horses, watching to see how the white flag was greeted. The three appeared so unexpectedly in the camp that the soldiers, taken unaware, were alarmed Catching sight of the five in the background and jumping to the hasty conclusion that they were advance spies for an approaching war party, twenty men set out to charge them. The horses wheeled, the soldiers fired, and in the melee two Indians were killed. There was bedlam in the camp. No one followed orders, if any were given. One of the three Indians with the white flag was shot down.

A few miles away, Black Hawk was giving a party. It was an elegant dog feast, given for Shabbona and Waubansee and a few other influential Potawotamis, in the hope of getting some reinforcements. When the survivors of the truce band came pounding into the middle of the party, it quickly broke up.

There was immediate action in Black Hawk's camp. When the white men, baying like hounds and yelling like idiots, set off in pursuit of the few Indians who had fled so nicely, they were neatly ambushed by Black Hawk. Suddenly, wherever they looked, there were savages firing from the bushes and from behind trees, while over the crest of the hill came a solid line of yelling, whooping, painted Sacs and Foxes, brandishing tomahawks or guns and firing as they came.

Stillman's men stopped as if struck. One horrified look told them all they needed to know. *The Indians were on the warpath*. Wheeling, the soldiers fled to their camp, screaming:

"Injuns! Injuns! The Injuns are comin'! *Run for your lives!*"

Sheer panic routed an army which, in most ordinary circumstances and in most known danger, probably would have stood its ground and fought to the last man. But panic was something which took hold of a man and destroyed his nerve. It blanked his mind and sent him running after his fellows, or trampling them if they got in the way.

When Stillman's Defeat was over, twelve Americans lay dead on a battlefield in northern Illinois. They were not ordinary dead. The Indians had hacked, mutilated, decapitated, scalped them. The burial detail next day, led by Captain Lincoln, had a rough time doing its job.

May 15, 1832, and the governor called for two thousand more men to rout the Indians, once and for all. Mild tactics, the "Be Kind to Indians" movement, hadn't worked. Now it was force, and only force, which must obliterate them. Stockades and forts were built hastily in northern Illinois, in the lead-mines country near the Mississippi and up in Wisconsin. Black Hawk and his band, on the warpath in earnest now, were killing and burning in unexpected spots as they pushed north. There were attacks up along the Rock River, a massacre of fifteen people at Indian Creek, a battle on the Pecatonica, an attack at Apple River Fort, and a dreadful massacre at Kellogg's Grove.

The Indians were well ahead of the pursuing soldiers and were hitting without any apparent plan, so that the army could not catch up. Then, suddenly, there appeared to be a reason for the places where Black Hawk was striking. He was working toward the north and west, and that meant he was going to try to cross the Mississippi to safety. The pursuit was heightened. The army left off following in his path, and went more directly up the river. A gunboat, the *Warrior*, came along with supplies.

August, 1832, and Black Hawk and his harried people, the women and children somehow keeping up, though often suffering in the long forced marches, reached the Mississippi, near Bad Axe River in Wisconsin.

Black Hawk sent some of his people to cross, while he and twenty warriors deployed the soldiers who were close on the trail.

The battle was a dreadful one. The flood plain of the Mississippi is broad at this point, with high hills rising from the Iowa and the Wisconsin lowlands. Many islands stud the river and numerous small tributaries flow into it.

When fogs were rising from the river an hour after sunrise, that placid summer morning, and the Indians were hastily crossing under their protective cover, the soldiers attacked. The retreating Sacs on the hill led the soldiers down to the river shore, where several were felled by Indian bullets. The Sacs fought from tree to tree, and when they reached the river, they were charged by bayonets until they were waist-deep in the water. Some swam, some hid in willow islands, but the band was all but wiped out. The battle ended in the Mississippi itself, which was streaked with blood as the maddened white soldiers scalped the Indians. Meanwhile, the canoes full of women and children and men were fired on, and a great mortality took place among them as canoes were capsized Many of the women were dressed as men, and the soldiers, besides, were in no mood for discrimination. At that point, all they wanted to do was kill Indians, any Indians, and finish the fight.

Twenty-four soldiers were killed. One hundred and fifty Indians died, and many were captured.

But Black Hawk escaped. He could always manage to get away. During the heat of the fight, when he saw how it was going to end, he and the malignant Prophet slipped off. They knew the fastnesses of the Dells of the Wisconsin River, and once there, they were well hidden. No soldiers could travel those intricate sandstone alleys and canyons and not be at the mercy of Indians hidden there, ready to pick them off one by one.

General Atkinson, however, knew that other Indians could do it. He sent two friendly Winnebagoes, who knew the area well, to bring in the Black Hawk and the Prophet.

Like panthers, the One-Eyed Decori and Chaeter, the Winnebagoes, relentlessly trailed the sandstone paths. Once they passed beneath the very white pine where Black Hawk was hidden. At last they tracked him down. The Prophet was caught nearby and brought to justice.

Dressed elegantly in white tanned deerskin, the prisoners, who regretted nothing, were brought to Fort Armstrong. A cholera epidemic there, however, was very bad, so the valuable captives were taken by steamboat down to St. Louis. Lieutenant Jefferson Davis, who later became President of the Confederate States, was the officer in charge of conveying the prisoners down to St. Louis, where they were confined in Jefferson Barracks, chained, until their trial.

After his trial and a trip to Washington, during which Black Hawk seemed impressed with the enormousness of the country he had tried to conquer, if not with the enormity of his crimes, he was brought back and pardoned. He lived in Keokuk's village, a peaceful old man. He died of a bilious fever a few years later. And finally there was peace along the Mississippi.

CHAPTER THIRTEEN

1820: *"Great Hawk that fliest with the flying Sun!*
Between the Turquoise Sycamores that riseth,
Young forever,
Thine image flashing on the bright celestial River."
                    EGYPTIAN *Book of the Dead*

I F we perhaps take our stock of goods to the Mississippi," suggested John James Audubon, in desperation, to his business partner, Rosier, at Henderson, Kentucky, "we might sell it at Sainte Genevieve or Cape Girardeau. We might possibly get enough money to satisfy our creditors and save us from ruin. I know of no other way."

Audubon's shoulders slumped. He had tried so hard to be a good businessman, but something always went wrong.

"People in Kentucky do not buy," muttered Rosier. "Yes, let us go to the Mississippi!"

Ever since he had first heard of it, the Mississippi had called to John Audubon, had called with a most siren voice. Now, with ruin staring at him, the chance had come to see the big river at last.

The keelboat set out down the Ohio late in the autumn and met an early freeze, which was already filling the Mississippi with floating ice. Unable to cross to the Missouri shore, where the current was easier and the towns, which were the partners' goal, were located, the keelboat had to be taken by sheer manpower up the Illinois shore.

The crew, including Rosier and Audubon, cordelled the keelboat—pulled it with a rope—up the river, breaking a path where there was none, stumbling over beached driftwood and rack heaps. And Audubon, a great, strong, powerful, enthusiastic man who would have been an asset to any keelboat crew simply because of his muscles, busily watched for birds as he helped pull the heavy boat up the Mississippi.

But the river was freezing fast. One morning the keelboat was caught in the ice opposite Cape Girardeau. The crew and passengers made camp in the Illinois forest above the river.

To protect the craft and its cargo, the men felled trees, which they shoved into the slush, building up a breakwater to protect the boat from being ground to pieces by the crowding ice floes. More trees were cut down for firewood. The men heaped up an ample supply of seasoned downwood, left high and dry by old floods, which would serve as fuel for a long time. Next they set about rolling great balls of wet snow to construct a sheltering, circular wall, as boys build a snow-fort, and in the middle a roaring fire was built.

John Audubon was having a most wonderful time. Seasoned woodsman though he was, camping beside the Mississippi in winter was something new. Everything he saw, everything that happened, interested him mightily. It was too cold for him to paint, for his paint-water froze. He was, however, storing ideas in his head. They were ideas ranging from plans for a picture of the beautiful little green paroquets devouring the hard, spiny seeds of clotbur along the river bottoms, to plans for including the mammals of America in another series of paintings.

There was something new every day. One day a great flock of trumpeter swans circled over the river and came fluttering down to land on the ice. Wolves saw them, too, as Audubon did; the animals crept out on their bellies, closer, closer, saliva drooling because of their hunger and the nearness of food. But while the naturalist watched, the swans watched, and when the wolves had reached a certain point, the birds set up a wild clangor of tootling calls, and rose into the wintery air. They circled and came down below the wolves, who again approached hopefully, and again the birds got up in triumph and flew on. Like disappointed dogs, the wolves sat down on their haunches, tongues lolling, and watched the great white birds vanish from their reach.

Parties of friendly Osage Indians often came in the evening to the keelboat camp and visited, while Audubon entertained them by sketching their portraits.

The keelboat party was held up there on the Mississippi shore for six weeks, until at last the break-up came and the ice floes ground their way down the surging river.

On the journey across the Mississippi, over to Cape Girardeau and Sainte Genevieve, with the keelboat pushing between the remains of the ice, Audubon saw a bird which was new to him It was a big, brown eagle, soaring above the river, as the bald eagles did, as if looking for fish. Audubon then and there vowed that he would one day paint its picture and give it a name never before given to a bird—the Washington eagle.

The Washington eagle indeed was added to the collection of portraits of Birds of America, but it no longer retains the name which Audubon gave it that day among the Mississippi's ice floes. For the Washington eagle is simply the immature dark form of the bald eagle, common along the watercourses of America.

Trading over, his goods sold and spring at its peak, Audubon started back on foot to Henderson, through forests alive with migrating birds. Though he was eager to get back to his wife and son, he hated to leave the big river. The Mississippi called, and he knew he would return.

And the time came sooner than he could have thought. The store failed. Rosier went his way. Audubon was arrested for debt As a last resort, he declared himself bankrupt and was released from prison, a despairing and hopeless man.

Finally, in defeat, he and his family went back to Shipping-port, on the Ohio, their former home. Audubon for a while earned a meager living by painting portraits and doing odd jobs, but always the birds and the river called. He could not get them off his mind. When he should have concentrated on being a financial success, he thought of birds. Perhaps only Lucy, his wife, understood and knew that it was his destiny to think of birds and to paint their portraits.

With her encouragement, John Audubon determined to go back to the Mississippi. He felt that his bird paintings would be his greatest chance for fame and money. And the only way to complete them was to take the time and do it. Now!

At a time when he was accounted a failure by men, he would ignore failure and succeed at what he loved best. He would explore all the lower Mississippi, the gulf coast, Florida, even the mysterious Keys. He had no idea as to how he would finance himself or his family, but he was going anyway. Friends offered to take care of Lucy and his children, and so, with a free mind but an empty purse, John James Audubon squared his big shoulders, shrugged off worry, debt, grief and disappointment, and headed with his paints and paper for the Mississippi.

He secured free passage on a flatboat, in exchange for supplying the crew with game along the way. There were ten aboard, including Audubon and a thirteen-year-old boy named Joseph Mason. Audubon had taught young Joe a little art, enough to see that the boy had talent, and was taking him along as his assistant and apprentice, to the boy's deep delight.

The flatboat was ideal for Audubon's purposes. It never went fast. Because it was a trading boat which stopped at every landing and town, there were frequent halts all along the way. The weather was the best which October along the Ohio could provide, which meant that it was pretty wonderful. Every day Audubon and the boy, delighted and eager, went ashore for game. They hiked through the autumn forests, obtaining new birds to bring aboard, and met the more leisurely flatboat downstream a few miles. For an artist and naturalist, and to the boy, it was an ideal cruise, and they made the most of it.

Down the Mississippi at last! Audubon found the forests full of migrant robins and blackbirds, while over the river, over the flimsy boat and its crew, the great hordes of birds which had nested in Canada and in northern United States—the pelicans and plovers, the curlews and cranes, the ducks and doves and hundreds of other kinds, in the days before America's bird-life was cut down in numbers—were bisecting a continent on their way to their wintering grounds.

In November, snow geese from the crowberry flats of Hudson Bay whitened the sand bars. Blue geese flew in their wavy flight against dark storm clouds. Canada geese trumpeted as they came in long Vs and echelons down a gray and windy sky. Thousands were on the gravelly shores near Horseshoe Lake, in southern Illinois, thousands more downstream, and it seemed that there were millions of birds in the air, always coming, like the tremendous flocks of passenger pigeons. Great rafts of scaup ducks and mallards bobbed on the current in the middle of the river. There were tiny, puffy, black and white buffleheads and cock-tailed ruddies, and pintails and canvasbacks and redheads and goldeneyes. The river was alive with ducks, parting to let the flatboat go through. Hundreds of busy killdeers squeaked on the mud flats and looked chilly but determined, shoulders hunched in the November wind. Cormorants sat like black candles on every snag.

Down past the Tennessee shores and the Chickasaw bluffs, one of the men winged a bald eagle. Brought aboard for a while and tethered by one leg so that it could not escape, the bird provided the artist with the living subject which he always coveted in place of the dead one. He painted his bald eagle there, aboard the flatboat, as the bird devoured a Mississippi River catfish. It was the catfish and the eagle, preserved in immortality on Plate Number 31, in *Birds of America*. What we do not see, but can sense, is that Audubon used Mississippi River water itself for his watercolors on this voyage, used its liquid to moisten his cakes of color; he cleaned his brush in the river. This was, in every sense, a bird of the Mississippi.

A feeling of power, a consciousness of deeply welling and unquenchable enthusiasm was rising like yeast within the artist. When Audubon had finished the eagle, life-sized on his great sheet of paper, he knew he was going to succeed.

At Natchez, Joe Mason and John Audubon went ashore for several days. The two roamed the streets and earned enough money by painting portraits of people to buy some decent shoes and food. They lived aboard the flatboat, so they had no lodging expense.

From Natchez there was a sudden opportunity to go on to New Orleans by a keelboat, but in the flurry of departure, John Audubon went off without his priceless portfolio of paintings. The eagle, the ducks, the rusty blackbirds which had been painted on the flatboat journey were left behind.

There was nothing to do but wait until he reached New Orleans, which was not until early January. He wrote frantically back to Natchez, to try to locate the portfolio, but the chance that it had been found and would be returned was exceedingly dim. If he failed to find it, he would have all that work to do

over, and he had already spent too much time in getting anywhere with his paintings.

But fortunately, for posterity and the success of *Birds of America*, the portfolio of bird and plant portraits which had been
painted with water colors moistened with Mississippi water,
came back to him on the next boat down the great river.

In New Orleans, Audubon again had to earn money by painting portraits. Whenever he could, he and Joe went out into the
bayous and swamps, down to the muskrat marshes along the
Mississippi and near the gulf. They ranged out, day after day,
fighting mosquitoes and wind, but finding birds, new birds, to
add to the growing collection.

In New Orleans, they haunted the French Market, to see if
there was anything new among the songbirds offered for sale
as food. When Audubon had exhausted these, he paid some of
the Cajun trappers who regularly brought in birds for market to
bring to him anything different they found west of the river.

When financial failure again stared at him in New Orleans
and the supply of new birds seemed to be running out, he was
given a job at Oakley Plantation, up in West Feliciana Parish,
bordering the Mississippi. Through the area winds Bayou Sara,
which empties into the river opposite Pointe Coupee and a great
bend of the Mississippi. Audubon was to teach drawing to young
Eliza Pirrie for four months, with ample time for his painting
and collecting in summer and early autumn The job not only
gave him the sustenance he needed, but it put him squarely in
the middle of the wild creatures, with plants everywhere available and birds abundantly about him. Young Joe Mason went
along with him, of course.

This was heaven—or would have been, if Lucy and the boys
could have been there. Later on they came. Lucy taught as
governess at a neighboring plantation.

While Audubon was at Oakley, he painted many of the forest
birds which are most typical of the lower Mississippi Valley and

arranged them on the typical plants. The painted buntings are on the Chickasaw plum; summer tanagers on a vine bearing large, dusky purple, muscadine grapes; mockingbirds dramatically fighting a rattlesnake near a nest in the yellow jessamine which doubtless grew at the plantation. The mourning dove he placed on the white-flowered Stewartia tree; the parula warbler on Louisiana's unique red iris. John Audubon painted his famous wild turkey with a background of Mississippi River cane which grew so thickly along that stream, from Kentucky to the gulf. His phoebes, which could have been placed prosaically upon any old twig, were perched instead upon a branch of autumn cotton bolls, the white fibers already popping from the burs; and the bay-breasted warbler sits upon a flowering cotton twig.

As a setting for certain birds, he depicted the trees of the South as he found them near the Mississippi—black-poll warblers eating tupelo berries; the Carolina wren singing in a red buckeye; the white-eyed vireo, so common in the South, upon a flowering China tree. The alder flycatcher is shown with the corky twig of the sweet gum tree, the orchard orioles in a honey locust tangle; the yellowthroat upon water oak; the yellow-billed cuckoo on the papaw with its ripe fruits which are the color of the cuckoo's wing.

Audubon loved magnolias. They were abundant in the Mississippi back country. He used the eared magnolia for his picture of the Kentucky warbler, put the black-billed cuckoos on a great-flowered magnolia branch, the warbling vireo on swamp magnolia The elaborate southern crossvine, common in the swamps, intrigued him with its pairs of coral-pink and yellow trumpets. He used them in a number of pictures, from that of the bluejays to the downy woodpecker, the yellow warbler and the chuck-wills-widow.

Audubon, along the Mississippi, was doing more than turning out a lot of pretty pictures. He was painting atmosphere, painting the character of part of America, painting the setting of the lower Mississippi. He was delineating forever the contours and

colors of the plants and birds which lived as part of the Mississippi River, creating a composite portrait of living things which
would always be inseparable from that river and its personality.

These birds were part of its moods. The plants on which the
birds were painted were nourished on the rich bottomland earth
which once had been carried as silt in the river, and when they
died they added more nourishment to that earth.

In his monumental *Birds of America*, reprints of which are in
many a library and home today, one may trace Audubon's Louisiana birds, his Mississippi River birds, by their settings and by
their peculiar quality of "riverness." It is almost as if he had
dipped his brush in river water for all of them, not just alone
for those which he painted aboard a leisurely flatboat, drifting
with the current downstream to the land of his dreams. Some
men may have drunk the Mississippi, but John James Audubon
used it to paint imperishable masterpieces.

CHAPTER FOURTEEN

1844: "Dark behind it rose the forest,
Rose the black and gloomy pine-trees,
Rose the firs with cones upon them."
LONGFELLOW

WITH the going of the last glacier from Canada, the pine and hemlock forests came back to the North and stood, unharmed by man, for thousands of years.

A pine began with a single needle rising from the damp, cool sand which had been left by the glacier. The needle sprang from a winged seed which had flitted, twirling and dipping on the wind, until it lay upon the earth and rooted there. In a few seasons of life and growth, the single needle became a woody stem with clusters of needles, held in bundles of five in the white pine. It had become a little tree, then, but it was many years, a hundred years, two hundred years, before a white pine stood, majestic and tall, with a trunk five feet in diameter and a crown resting in the skies.

By then, the tree had survived all the hazards which beset young white pines . . . the grazing deer; the bear rubbing and scratching on the bark; the hunger of porcupines; the searing fires and the tearing winds; the heaviness of snow and the desperate clinging bulk of the ice storm.

The forest was a place of shadows and of quietness. In the hush of the trees, whose needles softly soughed high in the wind and sunshine, even the birds were seldom loud. Small, shy warblers and kinglets nested and flitted about up there, sang high among the blurred green flame of the needles. Chickadees explored the twigs, nuthatches curried the bark for grubs and spiders. Bird-voices were thin and small in the vastness, all but swallowed in the silence of trees.

The brown ruffed grouse, chestily strutting and sturdily drumming on a fallen log, was but a resonant, hollow, feathery concussion of sound which belonged in the pine forest, where the deer stepped lightly on the springy, fallen needles and the bay lynx leaped on furry paws.

Winter was even more still as snow piled about the tall trunks and weighted the boughs. Masses of snow slid off with whishing thuds to the drifts below. Sometimes, in the cold, a tree split with a great explosion, and then the northern world was deathly silent once more. The needles hung stiff and sere, as if frozen, but the chickadees still piped, the nuthatches still hunted insect eggs and the grouse left a feathery imprint, a maze of tracks, embroidering the drifts.

Then the axes came. Silence broke. Peace was shattered, the trees were destroyed, the magic of miles of deep, virgin forest was forever lost

For men had discovered the pine forests of Wisconsin and Michigan and Minnesota. To a country newly spreading westward beyond the Alleghenies, the need of lumber for houses had become imperative. Not for long would men be satisfied with a log cabin. The need was for planed pine planks, to build proper houses and barns, to erect towns and churches and shops. And the lumber was there for the taking, there at the top of the Mississippi and its conveniently placed tributaries—the Black, the St. Croix, the Chippewa, the Wisconsin. They were highways by which lumber could be brought to the eager people of the Valley.

Men went up there to see for themselves whether the reports were true. They came back, after a while, many of them with stunned expressions on their faces. They had experienced some of the greatest forestland in all of North America, had seen it with their own eyes, had heard the silence, and perhaps some of them had been afraid. But they had also seen trees in terms of so many board feet of lumber. Unbelievable millions of those board feet waited to be taken out of the standing live trees, fed into the saws of the lumber mill and sent south to build the American Middle West.

All winter, in the blue-shadowed snow, the forests rang with the noise of axes and saws, groaned with the sound of white pines dying. Into the bitter air rose the raw smell of fresh-cut pine and resin and the odor of crushed needles. There was the vari-tongued laughter and talking, the grouching and singing of lumberjacks, who were Swedes or half-breeds, or French Canadians, strong men accustomed to cold, hard work and the reckless business of dropping forest giants.

Men and oxen dragged out the huge white pine logs, piled them on the riverbank, to wait for the snow to melt, the ice to break, the river to open. Then the logs were shoved with pike-poles and peavies into the moving ice water and sent to the saw-mill below. A boom directed the plunging, unwieldy logs into a quiet bay or slough, where they waited their turn at the mill. Behind the mills the mountains of sawdust rose higher and ever higher.

The winter of 1844 was unusually severe in Wisconsin and Minnesota. Snow stacked tremendously deep. Ice on the lakes and rivers lay three feet thick, blue-white and dense as stone. Spring was fearfully slow in coming. It was mid-May, therefore, before the ice finally broke up and ground its way downstream.

The break-up—and suddenly the logs on the riverbanks were on their way. Bounding and plunging like unruly buffalo, bucking, piling up, grinding and leaping, plunging under, jumping out of the water, they raced downstream at great speed. Thousands upon thousands of choice white pine logs were fast bound for the sawmill near Stillwater on the St. Croix River, twenty-five miles from the Mississippi. But, as the big snow went off, the St. Croix was rampaging in a sudden flood. Too late, the word came to the loggers up in the back country to hold the logs.

So there they were, rushing in a mad stampede, pouring murderously into the St. Croix. The log drive was caught up furiously in the flood. Giant white pine logs might have been so many leaping, fighting matchsticks. Workers at the mill were alerted. They tried to corral the thousands of stampeding logs, but it was a futile, puny effort. Men stood helpless, canthooks in their hands, while some three million feet of logs went pounding by.

Some were tossed on to the shores like driftwood. Some went downstream and into the boom of another lumber company. It seemed quite impossible to gather up all that loose timber and get it back up to its rightful mill. Logs went downstream so easily. Someone finally suggested that they be put together in rafts, to be sent down to St. Louis, the big market for lumber on the Mississippi. Before this, lumber had been cut into boards in the north before it was made into rafts for downriver shipping. Very likely, no one had ever sent raw, uncut logs down before, but it seemed the only way in which the runaway timber could be salvaged.

"I got a job for you, young man," the lumber company's manager said one May day, up along the St. Croix.

"Yes, sir," said Stephen Beck Hanks, aged twenty-three.

"You take notice of all those blamed runaway logs, don't you? Well, you use as many men as you need and put together as many rafts as the logs will make. No, don't ask me how, I sure don't know how! But the boss says ship them logs down to St. Louie as is, don't bother to cut 'em into lumber. As if we could, with them scattered from here to yonder! It's your job, Steve, to see they get there."

"Yes, sir," said Stephen Beck Hanks again, surprisingly delighted with the tough job facing him. Maybe no one had ever built a log raft. All right. So he would build one, do it the best way he could. With strong men to help, he hunted down the errant logs, day after day, week after week, corraled them together, one by one, and fastened them in rows, into a "string."

"That's the way," encouraged Hanks, watching as his men caught on. "Now you bore holes and put in bur-oak staples and birch branches, like we do for a lumber raft, to hold them tight. Same way, I guess. When you get a string that's long enough, start another. Ought to get a whole lot of rafts out of that timber, seems like." The tall, blue-eyed young man with the shock of light hair bent to help. He was generally considered to be the strongest fellow anywhere around.

This was almost to be expected, since Stephen Beck Hanks was a cousin to one Abraham Lincoln, who had made a name for himself along several rivers with his strength and his skill with river craft. Stephen was born in Kentucky in 1821. His father was Nancy Hanks Lincoln's brother, which made young Stephen first cousin to young Abraham Tallness and great strength seemed to run in that family. Stephen Hanks probably had that same look of goodness in his face which his older cousin possessed; Stephen was a kind, discerning man who was liked everywhere. That very goodness, his religious devotion, his curb on profanity and drinking, seemed to surround him with manageable men on the river in an era in which violence was common.

In the winter of 1837–38, when Stephen was only sixteen and was having to support his family after his father's death, he set up a small sawmill near his home at Albany, Illinois, beside the Mississippi above Rock Island. That winter he went up along the river, getting out some timber for his mill, to supply lumber for the new houses of settlers who were coming out to Illinois. This portion of the Mississippi provided only hardwood—maples and oaks and sycamores and hickories—but it was good enough for the building purposes at hand, perhaps a good deal better than softwood. People wanted pine as they had known it in the East, though, pine to build cities.

In 1840, the young man, not yet twenty years old, hired out to a St. Louis lumber man. The two walked north into the great white pine wilderness, to pick out timber. Up there in the deep snow and cold, Stephen worked with the lumbermen in getting out the logs, supervised the drive to the mill—and at that point he went to work to learn how to make a lumber raft.

With the raft huge and complete, the voyage began When Stephen Hanks's raft started out below Stillwater and got into Lake St. Croix, that wide place in the river of that same name, he put up a sail The men told him it would help when there was a little wind, because the current was so slow that it took forever and a day to navigate the length of the lake in calm weather. The wind, however, happened to be blowing the wrong way, so the sail did nothing to assist. Hanks ordered it hauled down. The water was calm, no current, not enough motion to float a feather, and here was an acre and a half of solid lumber needing to be guided down to the Mississippi.

The oars were little better. Poling didn't carry the raft far, either. In the pleasant May weather, the lake was a blue mirror, and the raft dallied upon it, going nowhere in a most leisurely manner.

"I declare, I don't see how we're going to get this lumber to the Mississippi before the Fourth of July!" exclaimed the tall young pilot in exasperation. "I never saw such a snail for speed!"

"Well, I reckon we got to make a line-and-anchor trip, then," said a grizzled raftsman glumly. "Though I can't hardly think of no work that's tougher nor more purely aggravatin', and that's a fact!"

"Yeah," agreed the others, looking moodily at the smooth lake.

"Maybe I don't rightly know what you mean by line-and-anchor," put in Hanks cautiously.

"Oh, well, we'll soon show you, son," said Elias Bills, who was as tall as Stephen Hanks, but twice as thick through the middle. "We've a-done it plenty times!"

So Big Elias went out in the skiff and rowed off ahead with a line that uncoiled until it stretched for almost half a mile. Elias rowed until he found shallow enough water and then dropped a heavy anchor overboard. With widening rings, it went in with a splash. He stood up and waved his red handkerchief. At this signal, the crew back on the drifting raft began to haul in on the line, hand over hand, until its massive loops lay dripping at their feet.

By that time the raft had been manually toted up to the skiff and the anchor. While the men dropped to the raft to rest and wipe their streaming brows, Big Elias again rowed ahead a half mile, paying out the line, and at his signal the raft crew once more pulled in the line until the great raft had moved painfully another half mile. This was repeated all the rest of the day, and all that night, too, the men working in shifts, Stephen Hanks helping in his turn. If he had thought that building a raft was hard, he knew now that there were harder jobs!

Finally Stephen Hanks saw the Mississippi ahead, and the raft slid into the faster-moving waters of the big river.

One evening when it was too murky to see farther, the Hanks raft pulled in and moored below the bulk of Barn Bluff, near what is now the town of Red Wing, Minnesota. It was a beautiful spot, the last sunset dying the water and reflecting on the eastern bluffs. However, the place quickly took on a less pleasant aspect. Other people were already camped there—Indians.

"The Sioux!" muttered Big Elias to Batiste, the Canuck. "I bet you they cause us plenty trouble before this night is over!"

"I bet you my life, yes! See, they come already!" exclaimed Batiste.

Stephen Hanks could do nothing to stop the Indians who, somewhat the worse for drink, swarmed over the raft. They looked at everything and poked into everything, wolfed unguarded food and loudly demanded whiskey and gunpowder.

"Take it easy, brothers," said Stephen Hanks calmly, his blue eyes boring down at the dirty visitors, who seemed to be somewhat in awe of his bulk, height, and air of authority. "We have no whiskey or powder for you. Wait your turn and you shall have food. Gregor," he called to the cook, who was hidden in the shack, afraid to come out, yet guarding with his life his precious food supplies. "Bring out those fresh fried-cakes and pass 'em around."

The Indians examined the doughnuts with considerable suspicion, and some risked a bite. Most of the cakes vanished the rest of the way, but a few of the more surly braves looked down on such puny fare and tossed them scornfully into the river. The visitors still wanted whiskey.

"We have no whiskey," Hanks patiently repeated, standing his ground.

The Indians, thwarted in their demands, nevertheless continued to carouse over the raft. The men were afraid to go to sleep. It was a miserable and alarming night to the crew, many of whom expected to be scalped before morning. They knew that this very thing had sometimes happened to raft crews in the wilderness of the upper Mississippi.

When dawn began to show behind the bluffs, Stephen Hanks told the Indians to get off. Some of them obeyed, but others surlily remained. Hanks ordered lines cast off and calmly made out into the river. At this, the remaining Sioux, awakening to what was happening, whooped loudly, dived into the river and got themselves ashore, to the considerable relief of the crew.

The raft proceeded on its slow way. It maneuvered the bends by means of the steering oars, manned at the ends of each crib of lumber. Sometimes in working the raft around a tricky twist, all the oars were pulled so hard that the raft curved like a great letter C before it got around and straightened out again.

The next trouble spot lay ahead: Lake Pepin. It was voted by the majority of river men as the place most cordially hated on the whole river. They agreed that the Devil himself lived here, which accounted for the sudden extremes of weather, the violence of the storms, the ability of ice to catch and crush boats, as well as winds to tear up lumber rafts and toss them in all directions.

Sometimes, it was true, Lake Pepin was wild and stormy, but on this May day it was so peaceful that there was no wind at all, and hardly any current worth mentioning. The raft, therefore, had to travel the length of Lake Pepin, a distance of twenty miles, by means of the old reliable line-and-anchor method, which wore blisters on everyone's palms and frayed everyone's patience.

Captain Hanks had taken on another raft which they had met downbound. The two were tied together lengthwise, for better strength against the wiles of the lake. Inch by inch, the two rafts were hauled part way down the lake, when suddenly out of nowhere, as Lake Pepin's private Demon delights to do, a wind got up and shoved hard from the south against the rafts. The oarsmen rowed frantically to turn toward the nearest shore, where they contrived to get the two big rafts into a slight shelter.

And there they stayed for three long, tiresome days, while the wind blew a half gale and waves ranted past like ranks of unicorns across the lake. The men, to while away the time, decided to go exploring.

"Exploring!" exclaimed Stephen Hanks. "In this wilderness?

I sure wouldn't advise it, fellows, not with the kind of country it is, and Indians around, and all. You better stay close."

Most of the men were older than he, and consequently they felt better qualified to judge as to what was wise or foolish. Ignoring the young man's warning, the whole crew trooped ashore, leaving Hanks resolutely on the raft. In not too long a time, however, the men were back. They looked considerably shaken.

"Well?" asked Hanks, smiling at their pale faces.

"Snakes!" exclaimed Gregor tersely. "Rattlesnakes! Dozens of 'em, hundreds of 'em, maybe thousands. For a while there, I think it looked like there was nothin' *but* rattlesnakes up there!"

"Yeah, top of the bluff," said Big Elias, looking at the club he held, fang marks visible on it. "We stepped right into 'em."

"We go by that trail, there," put in Batiste excitedly, pointing and waving his hands. "Up, up, we climb like the squirrel, yes. Then what does this Elias do, him, but step up on top the bluff, there, and he yell out, loud as anything:

" 'Yow! Snakes!' he say. And he step back so sudden, he pretty near knock down Gregor, who was right behind. So Gregor tramp on the toes of me, Batiste, and I yell at him, 'You watch where you step, you son of a caribou with the big feet!' So we shove forward, and there we stand, us, right in the nest of the rattlesnake!"

"Just come out of their den from the winter sleep," put in another man. "Steve, I tell you there was hundreds. We laid about us with sticks and rocks and got a lot of 'em, but I never want to be that close to so many rattlers again in all my life. That was close enough for me, their ugly heads cocked and the tongues runnin' in and out, and the tail rattles buzzin' like a swarm of bees."

"After this, maybe you better stay on the raft," Stephen Hanks suggested mildly. "I hear that sometimes snakes even come aboard rafts, but you don't have to invite trouble by going out to meet them!"

Finally, the wind laid and the raft crew thankfully went on down the Mississippi. Stephen Hanks was not as well acquainted with the river in those days as he was to be a little later. Now, when he was faced with the many apparent channels and the islands of the upper river, he was puzzled as to which was the best one to follow. Once, he headed down a stretch he felt was right, a nice broad reach. This, however, suddenly and treacherously narrowed around a bend. The leading raft forthwith grounded, and the second raft, piling up on it, broke it apart. And when a lumber raft smashes, it means a long, tiresome pickup job to get it all back together again. So Stephen Hanks and his men got busy and picked up boards, thousands of boards.

Days later, they finally got all the lumber, except that which had splintered on the impact, or had floated downstream They put it all back into the cribs. The two rafts went on their way. . . . And very next day they were smashed on Trempeleau Island. And there was the whole long, weary job of picking up and putting back together to do all over again.

They had to split the rafts to get through the aggravations of Coon Slough, around Devil's Elbow and through Crooked Slough, which lived up to its name. With rest and refreshment at Prairie du Chien, the hard-working crews went on with their lumber raft.

At the main stretch of the LeClaire Rapids, above Rock Island, the rafts were split again and were taken by a special rapids pilot safely to Davenport bridge. After that it was clear sailing. By July 12, the lumber was delivered to the St. Louis company which had ordered it so matter-of-factly. Hanks and his men walked back home.

And still out of the north came the big log drives in the spring, and still out of the rivers came the lumber rafts—until that spring of '44, when the log drive down the St. Croix overshot the boom and was gathered up at last, to go south as the first log raft on the Mississippi.

In a little while, the superiority of a raft of logs sent to saw-mills set up where people were building towns cut down the output of the lumber rafts. Pretty soon, it was mainly log rafts of great size which were coming down the river, millions of feet of logs out of what seemed to be inexhaustible forests, down to the waiting sawmills.

It was Stephen Hanks with his first log raft who decided that it would be more efficient and considerably faster to get through a becalmed Lake Pepin by hiring a steamboat to pull his logs rather than to endure the line-and-anchor chore. It was years later, however, when the first steamboat built expressly to tow rafts down the river was constructed and put to work on the upper Mississippi.

Maneuvering a log raft was a ticklish business for a steam-boat For one thing, there was a different sort of steering prob-lem. At first, when a steamboat attempted to push a raft, it usually swung cantankerously crosswise, at which moment the current usually caught and shoved it into the bank. However, a donkey engine was rigged with lines which would turn the steamboat at various angles to the raft, effecting a successful steering. Often there was a steamboat at the stern and another at the bow of a great raft. The new era of steam towing of log rafts opened. Naturally, one of the first of the new raft-boat pilots was Captain Stephen Beck Hanks.

And Stephen Hanks, raft by raft, boat by boat, learned the river. He continued to haul logs out of the north, to build houses in Illinois, Iowa and Missouri. He was an expert raft pilot in summer, an expert steamboat pilot on the lower river in winter. And it is said that, in the winter of 1852–53, when he had a job on a fast steamer between St. Louis and Alton, he took several quick trips up to Springfield, on his days off, to meet his cousin, the lawyer, Abraham Lincoln.

But Mr. Lincoln was away, riding the circuit, Mrs. Lincoln said, suspiciously eying the sun-browned, tall man with the blue eyes boring down on her, and he wouldn't be back for days, she fancied. She didn't invite the riverman in for tea. Hanks kinfolk, she felt, were somewhat beneath her. So the eminent Captain Hanks evidently never met the eminent Abraham Lincoln, who was also a riverman at heart and as much in love with boats and the rivers as Stephen Hanks himself.

As a raft-boat pilot, Captain Hanks had a lot to learn.

"You reckon I can do it?" he asked doubtfully when he first heard about the position. He had been off the river for some time. "Yes, I know, I've piloted rafts and I've piloted steamboats, but never the two together!"

The logs were waiting for him and his steamboat up in Cattail Slough, where they had wintered, all shipshape and solid. Pushing the raft, Captain Hanks made the Davenport bridge all right —he knew the tricks of current around that one—but at the Burlington bridge he struck a pier and suddenly his logs were floating off in all directions except upstream. While Captain Hanks fumed at his own stupidity, the men got to work collecting the logs and finally put the broken raft back together again.

He expected to split the raft and take the parts through the narrow Keokuk bridge one at a time; it could not, in fact, be pushed or pulled through otherwise. But when the time came to take the raft apart, it refused to budge. The parts clung together as tightly as glue In consequence, the broad raft struck both sides of the place through which it had been expected to pass. Once more, the Mississippi was strewn with floating logs.

They were patiently gathered up and returned to the raft. Next came Quincy bridge. This time the raft split properly. Hanks sent the mate ahead with the first section, and with the boat pushed the second. Thereupon, with only half a raft, he proceeded neatly to hit the Quincy bridge pier. For an expert raftsman and pilot, this was humiliating in the extreme, but it didn't happen again. After that, he held to his old authority and ran his bridges correctly and with ease up and down the Mississippi.

After fifty years of piloting on the big river, Captain Stephen Hanks was prevailed upon to retire at last, but each year he rode the river just to look at it.

And the years went by, as a man's life goes by, and the forests up in the north, the great, beautiful, splendid virgin white pine forests in the basins of the Wisconsin, the St. Croix, the Chippewa, the Black and the upper Mississippi above the Falls, were all but gone. They had been ruthlessly cut and sent downriver as logs. Only small second-growth trees, with a few forgotten old trees here and there, replaced those superb and incomparable ancient forests.

In August, 1915, when both the lumbering industry and the Steamboat Era seemed finished, ended, dead, the last lumber raft was put together on the upper Mississippi. It was made of boards gathered up from mills that were now idle for lack of trees. The old steamboat *Ottumwa Belle* was engaged to push this last raft down the river on a sentimental journey which would close a period in the history of the Mississippi.

At Albany, Illinois, an old gentleman of ninety-four, Captain Stephen Beck Hanks, came aboard, and once more he stood in the pilothouse and watched his river open before him, around one bend after another. In one man's full lifetime an era had come and gone, but the river was still there, still the old Mississippi, ready for what would come next.

And today, though lumber rafts are no more, there are still log rafts, not so great in size, perhaps, either in acreage or in the girth of the logs, but basically like those early rafts, still part of the Mississippi.

CHAPTER FIFTEEN

1848: *"We have obtained a land of promise, a land
which is choice above all other lands."*
BOOK OF MORMON

ADONIRAM BIXBY finished feeding the hogs and shut them
into their shed for the night. Too many wolves in Iowa for
a hog or shoat to be safe out of doors after dark. As he turned
to go into the house, Adoniram Bixby caught a sudden glare of
light over to the east and whirled to see what it was.

Fire! Something mighty big was burning on the hill across the
Mississippi in Illinois . . . right about where the Mormons had
their outlandish temple-church. Hardly anyone was left in the
city of Nauvoo, which the Mormons had built over there. They'd
cleared out when the citizenry got mad, after Joe Smith, called

their prophet, had been murdered by a mob. The Mormons had all gone, Mr. Bixby knew, but they'd had to leave their homes, most of them a whole lot grander than his own log house on the Iowa hill. They'd left the temple, too, not quite finished and only used for a couple of months, he'd heard, and it had cost a fortune.

Mr. Bixby stared in uneasy fascination at the way the leaping scarlet and yellow flames lit up the sky and poured a vast mushroom cloud of smoke studded with flying sparks into the autumn night. He turned and ran to the house.

"Ma, come quick!" he yelled. "The Mormon temple's a-burnin'!"

Mrs. Bixby, wiping her hands on her apron and followed by half a dozen little Bixbys, ran to the door just as a distant roar met their ears. A great geyser of sparks and burning embers in the conflagration rushed upward. After that, the fire died down somewhat.

"Glory be!" cried Mrs. Bixby, hand to her throat. "What on earth was that?"

Adoniram Bixby looked shaken. "The walls must've fell in," he murmured, staring across the river.

In the tremendous heat of the conflagration, the limestone walls of the Mormon temple, three stories high, had indeed fallen inward in a calcined heap. The metal figure of the angel Moroni blowing a trumpet, which topped the great edifice, broke loose and plummeted like a meteor through the flames. It landed near the baptismal font whose twelve majestic stone oxen were blackened and charred.

At last the people who had been watching in awed fascination, both in Illinois and across the river in Iowa, went back to their houses, shivering, not alone with the autumn chill, and left the tragedy to burn itself out. The ruins smoldered for days, and when the remains were cool enough to touch, men and boys picked about among the blackened stones to see what they could salvage. There was little that had escaped the great heat. Even the angel Moroni was gone, marked only by a little heap of metal which someone may have picked up and later on melted down to use for bullets.

In 1839, the Mormons had sought haven in Illinois. Exiled from New York State and from Ohio, persecuted and murdered by mobs in Missouri, and desperate and harassed people, under the leadership of the one they called their prophet, Joseph Smith, whose vision on the Hill of Cumorah had founded a new religion, came at last to Illinois. Oregon was too far. California was too far. These territories were outside the United States and so would be safe from the harrying of intolerant Americans. Galland's Bog, however, was nearer. And Joseph Smith chose it for his City of Saints.

Galland's Bog filled the big lowland of the Illinois shore where the Mississippi River curves in a great crescent above Keokuk and below Fort Madison. There had been an Indian village in this bottomland long ago, and, more recently, a village called Commerce, which did not and never would amount to much because of the soggy ground and the malaria mosquitoes which dwelt in hordes in these bottoms. The combination of cattail swamp, marsh and lowland forest was perhaps as unlikely a spot as Joseph Smith could have chosen on the entire length of the upper Mississippi. But in spite of the protests of his leaders, who could see and feel the mosquitoes and snakes and bog holes where Smith could see only lotuses, wild lilies, singing birds and a shining city called Nauvoo, the Beautiful, the prophet bought Galland's Bog. It was cheap, and he could afford it; whereas more desirable land would be costly, and other people would covet it. What Joseph Smith wanted was land which no one else valued, and if it had to be acres of cattails and redwinged blackbirds, swamp forest, poison ivy and stagnant water, then that was what he must buy. When the sale was completed, the land belonged to him and his people, all its mosquitoes, bog-suckers, shitepokes, bullfrogs, blackbirds, cockleburs, cattails and water snakes—and all its latent dreams.

From a distance, the Illinois and Iowa farmers watched as the

Mormons went about digging ditches and laying tile to drain the bog. They plowed up the cattails and actually laid out streets in an orderly and citified way, cut down the big syca- mores and soft maples and bur oaks and began to build houses along the still muddy streets. The houses were what amazed the outsiders. They themselves still lived mostly in log houses, only the most affluent aspiring to brick or clapboard, but not the Mormon houses. Some started out as log cabins, it is true, but even these were elegant affairs, two-storied, with glass-paned windows and planed floors. Brick-making was established and some wonderful brick mansions went up.

The city did not rise easily nor smoothly nor in a night. By the end of that first summer, a large percentage of the encamp- ment had been laid low by dreadful attacks of malaria and typhoid. Men and women and children miserably shook with ague and burned with fever. Some of them died. Death and failure suddenly lay everywhere in the steaming, half-cleared, stump-filled, muddy, mosquito-infested acres of Galland's Bog, around which licked the Mississippi. But the prophet would not be conquered. With supreme faith, invoking the help of God, he went about and healed many of the sick through the power of prayer. And both the people and the city rallied, rose and finally prospered.

When it was completed, Nauvoo, Illinois, was as fine and beautiful a city as Joseph Smith had prophesied—and upon which he almost fanatically had insisted. Streets were broad and long, bisecting each other at neat angles. Between seven thou- sand and eight thousand houses of brick, clapboard, or log—fine, big houses with glass windows, skillfully made doors and many chimneys smoking to the winter sky—lined the streets.

With the city built and prospering, Joseph Smith planned the Church of Mormon. It would be a temple like nothing ever erected in America, the grandest edifice beside the Mississippi. He ordered it placed at the top of Nauvoo hill, to the east of the lowland, so that the temple would be seen by steamboats coming up or down the river, would be visible from out on the Illinois prairie and from Iowa across a mile of Mississippi water.

Just as he had written the strangely fabricated Book of Mormon, so the Mormon temple was a curious combination of architectural styles and symbolism made concrete by the force of Joseph Smith's will. Limestone, laid down millions of years before by a long-gone sea, was quarried several miles away and the great blocks hauled to the temple site. Fine timbers were hand-hewn by the dedicated Mormons, who put their best workmanship as a tithe into the erection of the temple.

There were three floors in the rectangular, million-dollar edifice. A basement housed the enormous baptismal font, which was held by twelve massive stone oxen. The whole church was topped by a tall cupola holding a fine statue of the Mormon angel Moroni. The three main floors of the building had stone walls, but the upper parts were of wood. Extending two stories high were thirty stone pilasters, carefully spaced. The base of each was formed by a stone block bearing the figure of a large crescent moon, points turned down. The capstone of each pilaster was a figure of a sun with a fat, cryptic face, surrounded by rays and topped with two hands holding trumpets. Above these sunstones were blocks bearing stars. The figures were symbolic, and all had their meaning.

Twenty thousand people lived in Nauvoo in the 1840's. This was a greater population than Chicago or any other city of Illinois had at that time. Nauvoo, however, became a powerful community which voted in a bloc, and this alarmed the state of Illinois with fear of political monopolies. Then, as a climax of power and success, Joseph Smith, perhaps unwisely, announced that he would be candidate for President of the United States. He confidently sent his missionaries out to electioneer for him.

This was the last straw. The people of Illinois, in some irritation, had watched Nauvoo a-building and had had to admire how the once-persecuted Mormons triumphed over their adversities. It was harder to accept their high-handed superiority, their one-track voting habits and the effrontery of their leader in actually running for President of the United States. At that rate, people muttered heatedly, the entire country would be Mormon within a decade. The whole dreadful discontent came to a head when word got out that Mormon men were taking more than one wife apiece, that polygamy was acceptable and legal. Politics was one thing, but immorality and going against the laws of God and the United States of America were quite another. The non-Mormons nearest Nauvoo boiled over.

From that time on, the Saints were in danger of their lives. Joseph Smith and his brother, Hyrum, were arrested and held for safety in the stone jail at Carthage, a few miles from Nauvoo. But while Governor Ford of Illinois was in Nauvoo, assuring the alarmed people that the Mormons and their leaders would have a fair trial, the Smiths were dying in the Carthage jail. The mob could not be held back. Shots were fired. Both brothers were killed.

With this tragedy, life in the beautiful city came to a halt. People stayed in their homes. They spoke fearfully of what might happen next. Missionaries came hastily back to Nauvoo for further orders. There were armed clashes with outsiders, and there was always the possibility that the mobs would get out of hand, descend on the city and utterly destroy it and the people. In a land of freedom of thought and worship, the Mormons along the Mississippi had neither.

With the Smiths murdered and people coming out openly to battle the Mormons wherever the occasion rose, their new leader, Brigham Young, knew they would have to leave the unfinished temple and the city and find a better haven. This time they would go outside the boundaries of the United States— to Utah.

"When grass grows in the spring, we go!" announced the forceful Brigham Young. The people, given courage by his strength, worked all that winter to make wagons and repair

harness and clothing. They sold their property and the possessions which could not be taken along, to prepare for the exodus.
It was a tremendous undertaking, which had to be arranged
and carried out with care, for twenty thousand people cannot
be casually transplanted without considerable anguish, labor
and expense.

Brigham Young planned it well. They would leave in detach-
ments. Each party would plant seed along the way for the next
company to harvest. They should set out a number of weeks
apart so that there would not be too great a drain upon the
country through which they traveled. With groups preparing
food for the next, everything would be well, and they would all
eventually reach the haven in Utah.

But when, in midwinter, a warrant suddenly came for Brigham
Young's arrest and the immediate evacuation of the city, he
knew he had not enough time for the excellent plans that had
been made. To leave now, however, in midwinter, would be
suicidal, but the unheeding orders would not listen:

"Go now, or be imprisoned."

In February, 1846, the Mississippi lay frozen from its source
to a point below St. Louis. Nearly a mile of glare ice lay between Nauvoo and the Iowa shore. Across it whipped a cutting
wind, blowing stinging ice crystals into the faces of the people
and animals who obediently set out upon it. Behind them lay
the warmth and comfort of the now empty homes in Nauvoo.
Ahead lay the desolate snow covered Iowa hills. There was no
possible haven for a thousand miles, and the temperature lay
close to zero.

Patiently, and without revilement or question, five thousand
Mormons and their animals proceeded to obey the Governor's
order. Slipping and falling on the Mississippi's ice, they dragged
with them a few belongings, helped their children and cattle
and horses across the river. Perhaps never before nor since had
so great an exodus of human beings crossed the great river. Not

even the unhappy Cherokees on the Trail of Tears could equal it.

On the Iowa shore, Brigham Young, compassion in his eyes, waited for his people. When all had reached him, he dropped to his knees in the crusted snow and prayed, and the exiles knelt and prayed with him. On the eastern shore, the city lay quietly, as if awaiting death. From many chimneys no smoke rose.

The five thousand unprepared travelers struggled up the steep bluff and set out across Iowa. Seven miles from the river, they made camp. Food grew scarce; warmth was almost nonexistent; the temperature lay low; a blizzard blew out of the northwest. Hungry cattle and horses were reduced to eating bare twigs and bushes.

It was all Brigham Young could do to care for his charges, when, to his horror, another thousand people, disobeying his orders, came eagerly to join him. Back to Nauvoo went a blazing order to the rest of his followers to stay where they were until spring. He had all he could do to provide meagerly for those who had come with him.

But the remaining citizens of Nauvoo were frightened at the unbridled hatred of their non-Mormon neighbors and at the almost daily assaults on their persons and property. Without the strength of Brigham Young to guide and protect them, they felt deserted.

Iowa roads across from Nauvoo, heading toward the first group, became crowded with wagons and with families. By spring, they were leaving at the rate of a thousand a week. Instead of waiting to sow seed or come late enough for a harvest, the companies crowded too close together, and food along the line of march was terribly depleted. Twenty thousand men, women, and children with their animals cannot live off the country without reducing supplies alarmingly.

Eventually, after a harrowing and desperate migration in which many people died, the exiled multitude came to Utah territory, which at that time lay well outside the United States. There they built Salt Lake City. A new temple was constructed, topped with a new and triumphant angel Moroni. And the Mormons made the desert valley "to blossom as the rose."

Nauvoo was deserted. Weeds grew in the once carefully tended streets and gardens. Windows gaped and squirrels nested in the houses Paint dimmed, and there was a desperate air of neglect everywhere in what had become a ghost town along the Mississippi.

And on a night in October, 1848, when wild geese were heading south across the dark sky, the temple was set on fire by someone forever unknown. The flames leaped and roared and consumed the wooden portions of the great building. The geese that night were confused by the light. They circled, honking, until they found their way into the darkness again. The cupola burned and the angel Moroni plummeted to the basement. Only part of the limestone walls, blackened by fire, the cryptic smiles of the sunstones unchanged, still stood, a shell of departed glory and a reproach to every thinking man who saw it.

"With queer folk like them Mormon 'Saints,'" commented Adoniram Bixby righteously to Mrs. Bixby, who nodded sagely in confirmation, "you just never know what-all is goin' to happen!"

With which profound remark he applied himself with vigor to his dinner.

Some months after the temple burned, there set out, far down the Mississippi River at New Orleans, a steamboat loaded with hopeful people. They, like the Mormons, sought a new place in which to carry out their beliefs and way of life.

The reason for their being there at all had its origin in France, some years earlier, when the novelist, Victor Hugo, wrote about an ideal and idyllic way of life in a mythical land called Icaria.

A certain noted French jurist who became Attorney-General during the Second Republic, one Etienne Cabet, became inflamed by the communistic thoughts set forth in Hugo's novel. He planned a perfect community of people who lived and worked together for the equal benefit of all.

Etienne Cabet gathered around himself a group of followers who believed as he did, but found it difficult in France to carry out Icaria as he visualized it. The Old World was not receptive to his ideas, he declared in disgust. He would go to the free air of the New World which, he felt, would welcome him and his people, and would permit them to carry out their plans. He was completely ignorant of the nature of America, but when he learned that land in Texas was cheap, he felt that Texas, wherever it was and whatever it was, must be the place.

Cabet sent a group of responsible Icarians ahead to obtain land. He closed up his affairs in France and said his farewells, knowing he would never return. Before he landed in New Orleans, however, his advance guard, who had settled on the banks of the Red River, near Shreveport, Louisiana, had found the climate a violent one to live in. The land, besides, was far from what they had hoped to acquire. The people unhappily returned to New Orleans, to confer with M. Cabet when he should arrive.

Papa Cabet, as he was fondly called, was undaunted by his first failure in America. Shortly afterward, a news item in a New Orleans paper caught his eye. He read that the Mormon town of Nauvoo, up the Mississippi, had been evacuated and was now for sale—houses, furniture, land, everything.

Ah, this was it—Nauvoo. It lay nearly fifteen hundred miles up the great river which was sweeping in a huge, muddy curve around New Orleans. Nauvoo, in the heart of the continent, by means of the Mississippi was connected nicely with New Orleans, the outer world—and France.

"Go now," said Papa Cabet joyfully to three of his best men, "and take the next steamboat north up the Mississippi. Find this Nauvoo—ah, the curious, sweet-sounding name!—and if it be favorable, then buy for us as much of it as you have money for. We are, alas, limited in funds, but use what there is, and perhaps later we may be able to purchase more land when we have need of it."

The three Frenchmen examined the site of Nauvoo. The deserted city in the lowland was not for them, they felt, even if they could afford the great amount that was asked for it. They had heard of Mississippi floods while they were in New Orleans and were not as trusting as the Mormons in believing that the lowland would always remain above water. But on the hilltop near the burned shell of the temple, whose eerie aspect fascinated them, they bought twelve acres of land. The three were passengers on the next steamboat going back to New Orleans.

The Icarians, as they called themselves, with Papa Cabet gaily leading them, came in 1849 to Nauvoo and set about to build a town of their own which was based upon some of the earlier habitations of the Mormons.

Buildings were large, to accommodate numbers of people living or working together. A huge communal hall was built. The first floor was used as a great dining room, or as an auditorium, with a seating capacity of twelve hundred. Northwest of the hall was a kitchen which was so efficiently run that the twelve hundred diners could be served almost at once. From kitchen to dining room, tracks were laid down on which cars loaded with food were sent to the 120 tables arranged in the great room. Paintings decorated the walls, together with maxims and mottos of the Icarian belief. Repeated throughout appeared the words:

"Everyone do according to his capacity."

Upstairs were comfortable living rooms and bathrooms equipped with hot and cold running water—that was in 1849, and such luxuries were rare. Elsewhere was a school, including separate dormitories for boys and for girls. A child was started in school at the age of seven and was kept right there. He seldom saw his parents, except for visits with them on week-ends.

There was a communal laundry, a bakery and other businesses, each run by men and women experienced in that field. For their work they received no pay. They and the others simply benefitted equally in their ration of food, lodging and clothing. There was free medical care, hospital care, recreation and education. There was an excellent orchestra in Nauvoo, a library and other cultural advantages.

Items which they did not make for themselves were purchased by the Icarians with the money obtained from the sale of flour, whiskey, pork, wagons, lumber—all of which were produced in the town. Cabet, however, wanted to discourage even this reliance on the outside world. He wanted Icaria to be a world apart.

With the Icarian principle working well, Etienne Cabet spent many hours in looking at the ruins of the temple. What a pity that such beauty should have been destroyed! If it could be rebuilt . . .

He would do it! At great expense to himself and to his people, Cabet set out to restore the Mormon temple. Some day, he felt, it would be called the Icarian temple, a monument to his dream. Alfred H. Piquenard, a Frenchman of the community who later was to design the Illinois state capitol building in Springfield, was sent north to arrange for timber with which to rebuild the upper portion of the temple in all its old grandeur.

The stones were carefully reset from where they had fallen. The charring was removed, so that the cryptic sun faces and the turned-down moons were as fresh as when they were first chiseled out of the Mississippi River limestone.

After much labor and expense, the exterior was nearly completed. It would take longer to finish the inside, but the shell of the wonderful building at last was standing tall against the western sky. Beyond and far below glittered the Mississippi.

One day that sky darkened ominously, until it looked almost as black as night. A wind got up which bellowed like sustained thunder in the distance. Men working on the temple threw down their tools, raced for the community hall and fled with their families to the cellar.

The noise drew rapidly nearer. Trees in Iowa were flattened. Branches and whole trees were whirled into the air. A waterspout was drawn up from the Mississippi and fell in a muddy rain, full of fish, over the flats.

The tornado struck the Mormon temple. The roar of the falling walls was heard three miles away.

The people in Nauvoo thought the world was coming to an end. They cowered in the cellars. But it was only the haunted temple returning to ruins. Only the temple had been singled out by the big wind for destruction. The rest of Nauvoo escaped harm.

Trying not to think of the terrible amount of money and time which had gone vainly into the ruined edifice—though his embittered followers pointedly reminded him of it many times—Cabet ordered the remains to be used in construction of the school and in other building work in Nauvoo. Most of the sunstones and moonstones either were destroyed or were carried away. Several moonstones still remain in Nauvoo—two, most fittingly, as tombstones for Joseph and Hyrum Smith, and one is in the hotel yard. A sunstone is in Quincy. Another was in Springfield for many years, but it was returned to Nauvoo in 1955 and set in the state park, just east of the old part of the town.

Etienne Cabet at last became the Supreme Dictator of Nauvoo. This, and the fact that although a communal plan sounds excellent in theory, it seldom works out well, caused a break-up in the once peaceful community. The individual personality had come to the top again. Leaders may encourage men to work according to their ability, but that ability differs with every man, and so does his ambition. When the skilled workman derives only as much benefit from his labor as the unskilled man or the lazy one, or the downright shirker, then he is bound to get angry finally and denounce the system which fosters such unfairness. The individual, Etienne Cabet discovered, cannot be smothered too long, especially in the free air of America.

This happened in Nauvoo to the Icarians. Everyone benefited alike, and pretty soon the lazy ones discovered they didn't have to work in order to be fed and clothed and entertained, to have their socks darned, their beds made and their aches doctored, so they quit working and sat back, played chess and waited to be cared for. There were financial difficulties, besides, for Icaria had gotten itself badly in debt.

And so a rift opened, and at the next election, in 1856, the once beloved Papa Cabet, no longer idolized, failed to be re-elected to the presidency of the community. Icarian Nauvoo began to go to pieces Some of the people moved to Iowa, to join others who had gone there earlier; the land was sold. Poor Papa Cabet, a defeated man, heart-broken at the failure of his dream, went to St. Louis, where he soon died.

Again Nauvoo, the haunted town, was deserted, until German farmers came in. They took over the French town on the hill, set up prosperous farms round about in the rich loam. Beautiful vineyards were planted for wine-making; a successful business in wines and blue cheese was developed.

Nauvoo eventually became an extensive Roman Catholic community, with a large church and convent school. The town is, however, still a Mormon center, a point of pilgrimage for thousands of Mormons every year.

Today, the living portion of the town lies chiefly on the hill, with the shadowy ghost town of the Mormons, but little populated, in the lowland. It is now part of the state park which is designed to preserve the area.

Past the big bend, the Mississippi still flows, spreads broadly among the shallows where herons wade, while ghosts of the past still walk in Galland's Bog.

CHAPTER SIXTEEN

1861: *"Let it roll on. Let it roll on full flood,
inexorable, irresistible, benignant, to
broader lands and better days."*
WINSTON. CHURCHILL

IT was the year 1861, and at Mile 947 above the mouth of the Mississippi, a great chain lay across the river. With huge links weighing fifteen pounds each, the tremendous chain stretched for more than a mile and was fastened to a six-ton sea anchor embedded in the Kentucky bluffs. The War between the States had begun.

The long, brown, liquid avenue of the Mississippi was closed. No Union boats could hope to pass, for even if they should somehow blast through the chain, a formidable battery of guns lay strategically on the bluff at Columbus.

"It's our river, keep out!" said the South, and built forts to guard it. To the North, this was an insult and a challenge. The North needed the Mississippi as badly as the South did. The latter wanted it for an open supply line to bring in food and materials from the western territories, which by their very distance were untouched by the war. The western rivers, connected with the Mississippi, could provide the South with all the food and forage it should require for a long and successful war.

President Lincoln, who knew the river and knew the South, also was aware of this. He said:

"The Mississippi is the backbone of the Rebellion; it is the key to the whole situation. But we must have troops enough not only to hold New Orleans, but to proceed at once toward Vicksburg, which is the key to all that country watered by the Mississippi and its tributaries."

Although the South held the lower Mississippi, there were only certain strategic spots below the mouth of the Ohio which could be fortified. The remainder of that great alluvial plain and delta country was too low, too swampy and too uncertain in time of high or low water to permit any fort to be built, manned, or held. But on the eastern shore of the river there were several notable places where a long line of bluffs extended close to the Mississippi, and it was on these that the South set its forts to effectually block and hold the mighty stream.

The first fort was located at Columbus, Kentucky, where General Polk's big chain lay across the river. Next downstream was dangerous Island Number 10, lying in the curve of the great S-bend above New Madrid. Then New Madrid itself was fortified. There was no fortification below that until one came to Fort Pillow, on the First Chickasaw Bluff. Memphis defended the Fourth Bluff

If the North should ever get as far as Memphis in opening the river, a possibility which no one in the South felt could ever occur because of the impregnable position of dangerous, bristling Island Number 10, then there would be no more forts for several hundred miles to challenge the invaders. But at Mile 430 stood Vicksburg, proudly called the Gibraltar of the Mississippi. No one would get past Vicksburg.

The town believed itself to be completely unassailable because of its peculiar position on the bluffs above a curious loop in the Mississippi, very different from what it is today. The curve of the Yazoo River lay around to the north and east, to protect the city from rear assault. Below Vicksburg was the fort at Grand Gulf, then came Port Hudson, Baton Rouge and New Orleans, with Fort St. Philip and Fort Jackson below.

Secure in its line of river defenses, the South felt that it would win the war as long as the lower Mississippi was held, together with the key to supply lines which it represented. At the same time, it kept the Northern boats bottled up and unable to make contact with trade, supplies and troops coming in via the Gulf of Mexico.

Railroads were comparatively few in the South. They were easily put out of commission by an enemy bent on tearing up rails and ties, but the river was always there, indestructible. Steamboats loaded with supplies could move more goods and men at a faster speed than railroads or the plodding mule wagons which were the usual mode of conveyance. Thousands of wheels and thousands of clumping hoofs dragging the food and supplies of an army on the march often hampered action and made a morass of the muddy roads. But the river . . . the river . . .

"We've got to keep the river," said the South.

"And *we've* got to take it away from you!" vowed the North, in growing desperation, and set about to do it And for possession of the river, during the War between the States, a series of campaigns were fought in the Mississippi Valley which probably were unlike any other campaigns ever fought in any war. Never before, perhaps, was there a river involved which was like the Mississippi. It refuted all the old army theories and the expert training of officers at West Point and Virginia Military Institute.

For the Mississippi made the rules, and men had to adapt themselves and their strategy to it, not it to them.

Grant couldn't hope to take the fort at Columbus, not with that chain in his way. So he by-passed Columbus and captured Fort Henry and Fort Donelson on the Tennessee and the Cumberland, fought the battle of Shiloh, and thus forced the evacuation of Columbus. But before Grant arrived to remove the chain, the guns and men had been hastily taken down to strengthen Island Number 10. No boat, it was felt, could hope to pass that formidable island-fortress, set squarely in the middle of the Mississippi.

Before it approaches New Madrid, the river swings in a backward-flung loop which sends the current northwest, curves around past the town of New Madrid at the west end of the loop, then heads due east a distance. The river starts south, finally, after having traveled some twenty miles in a bend, though the space between is less than a mile. Island Number 10 lay in the flow of the river at the beginning of the first loop. Nearby were the state boundaries of Kentucky, Arkansas, Tennessee and Missouri.

With 130 pieces of artillery added to the already strong fortification on the island, and 7,000 men to defend it, Island Number 10 was in an excellent location. In case of a battle, however, there was only one line by which supplies could come to the island, only one good road, that which ran from Tiptonville, Tennessee, between Reelfoot Lake and the bend of the river opposite the island. This also was the only road by which the 7,000 men could retreat from the island, if they needed to do so. It was vital to keep open the Tiptonville road.

The Union gunboats, built at St. Louis, were all upstream. They crowded impatiently, like cattle at a fence, afraid to risk an attempt to get past the deadly island. Union General Pope meanwhile set up his plans. He brought some twenty thousand men around New Madrid by land and stationed them at Point Pleasant, twelve miles below that town. In this way he cut off all the supplies coming upriver to New Madrid, as well as to the island. In ten days, New Madrid surrendered without a battle.

In the early spring of 1862, with the Mississippi flooding the bottomlands, Pope's plans proceeded. In his command was a battalion of Army Engineers. Three hundred men were set to work in relays. They stood on small rafts and cut off trees about eight feet above the water; while others roped the logs, they were snaked out with the help of steamboats. A huge saw on a pivot cut away the stumps close to the ground, underwater, and in nineteen days a channel, a clear water-road, six miles long, fifty feet wide and four and one-half feet deep, was cut through a submerged forest on the peninsula, to connect New Madrid with the gunboats lying upstream.

Small gunboats could get through, and did, carrying part of Pope's army over this improvised canal, but the larger boats were of too deep a draft to risk the stumpy channel. The gunboat *Carondelet* then took part in a boldly proposed plan. Protected with planks, heavy coils of rope and racks of chains, the boat was armored, while a barge loaded with hay was lashed in front of the powder magazine. The escape steam which normally would rush out, hissing and sputtering, from the chimneys, was sent through the wheel house, to make the boat almost silent.

At ten o'clock on the night of April 4, when the frogs were yammering away in all the flooded lowlands and clouds obscured the stars, lightning was flickering around the horizon and thunder began to rumble. At this tense moment, the *Carondelet* started out to run past Island Number 10. She went softly and trod silently, and all went well until she was almost abreast of the island, when suddenly fire burst from the chimneys Showers of sparks and burning soot shot into the darkness—without steam to moisten it, the soot had caught fire in the stacks. Startled, the guns on Island Number 10 roared. Thunder added to the din. The storm rapidly surged closer, lightning flashed brilliantly now, illuminating the scene, and the rain started on a high wind.

But the bold *Carondelet* had run so close to the fort on the island that the guns were aimed too high, and they overshot their mark, while the gunboat, with the current in her favor, scooted out of danger. By midnight she was safely in New Madrid, and the storm was dying away in the east. Next night, the *Pittsburgh* ran past the island, and meanwhile, General Pope came around and captured the vital escape route, the Tiptonville road.

That did it. The losses at Fort Donelson and Shiloh had weakened any support Island Number 10 might have had, and with the one line of retreat taken away, the island surrendered.

All seven thousand men were captured; so were the artillery, horses and supplies. And now the Mississippi was open as far as the First Chickasaw Bluff, on which stood tough Fort Pillow.

With the Southern defeat at Corinth, Mississippi, however, even Fort Pillow was evacuated, just as Columbus was. This left the river open as far as Memphis, on the Fourth Chickasaw Bluff. Belligerent Memphis, far from evacuating, had warships and gunboats ready and was grimly geared for a fight.

Up at St. Louis, James Eads was building ironclad rams and gunboats for river warfare. He had revolutionary plans for his ironclads and for a revolving gun turret which would swivel about with a murderous, raking fire. The Carondelet shipyard was busy on a twenty-four hour schedule. Snagboats were converted, steamboats were converted, and some boats were built expressly for the affair at hand. The ironclads were low slung, only a small part visible above the water. The deadly rams had iron beaks below the water line which gouged holes in wooden vessels. But when all these war boats were ready to fight, they could not reach the mouth of the river, where Admiral Farragut was trying to get in to capture New Orleans and Vicksburg.

In March, 1862, Farragut and his fleet of wooden sailing vessels, his flagships and his corvettes, his sloops and gunboats and mortar boats commanded by Admiral Porter, came cautiously into the mouth of the Mississippi. The big ships had a hard time getting over the mud bar at the mouth, since the water there was only about eight feet deep because of piled up sediment. But the warships were somehow dragged over the bar and finally stood at anchor in the lower Mississippi, less than a hundred miles below New Orleans, waiting. Ten miles ahead of the fleet lay two fortifications, Fort St. Philip on the east and Fort Jackson on the west.

Both were well armed and well manned. Besides, as an added assurance that no enemy ships could slip past, night or day, there had been stretched a line of old ship hulks, chained together across the river to form a strong blockade. The lines and masts had been taken down, thrown overboard and allowed to drag as a further menace to navigation. A dozen Confederate warships and a vicious little iron ram named the *Manassas* gathered in the vicinity of the forts.

By April 16, the Union bomb ships were anchored around the bend below Fort Jackson. Their masts were concealed with cut willow boughs, so that they looked like part of the swamp. For five days Commander Porter's cannon tossed 16,800 shells into that fort, but, although Fort Jackson was pretty well shot full of holes, there was no visible sign of surrender.

The formidable line of old ships, still rising and falling on the Mississippi current and completely blocking the river, irked the Northern ships downstream. On the night of the 20th, while Porter was still carrying on the bombardment with continued vigor, though not very much real success, two small Union gunboats, the *Itasca* and the *Pinola*, slid past the forts without being detected and tried to blow up the hulks barring the way. But the fuse misfired, and when the *Itasca* next tried to ignite the hulks, the current swept her out of control, entangled her with the wrecks, then ran her inshore until the gunboat was hopelessly aground. An alert enemy battery could have picked her off then and there. The *Pinola*, however, managed to drag her sister ship off the mud.

But while the *Itasca* was aground, her astute commander discovered that, between the first hulk and the shore, there was a narrow space of water through which a small, bold boat might pass—and get neatly above the line of rocking hulks. The *Itasca* thereupon did just that. She got well above, turned, then crowded on steam and headed straight for the chains. She struck, struck so hard that the bow of the *Itasca* was lifted straight into the air and for a moment she was standing almost on end, then came down hard—and the massive chains snapped.

The current of the river did the rest. It pushed the hulks to either side, and the *Itasca*, her commander and men grinning broadly, rejoined the *Pinola*. The two steamed in a hurry back to the fleet, to inform Farragut that now the way was clear.

At two o'clock in the morning, April 24, the squadron moved slowly up the Mississippi. Sandbags and cables protected the vital parts of the ships, and all seemed going well until the forts, tardily awakening to what was happening, let loose a blistering fire. The gunboats, thereupon, turned and bombarded the forts until they surrendered.

The Confederate ram, *Manassas*, however, darted viciously here and there, inflicting wounds. In the midst of the confusion, a great glare of fire appeared on the river. A small tugboat was valiantly shoving a raft of blazing pine knots straight at the *Hartford*, Farragut's flagship. The burning raft rammed against the hull, where the flames leaped to the rigging. The men worked fast. The fire was put out in time. The fleet steamed on, with only the *Manassas* tagging persistently along behind, like an annoying terrier, nipping at their heels and trying to inflict more damage.

Farragut's wooden fleet approached New Orleans. The city was in a dreadful turmoil of fear and hatred. Bales of cotton and other supplies were burning on the wharves. The populace met Farragut with knives and guns. The city, however, was easily taken. With the capture of the biggest city on its shores, the Mississippi was clear from the mouth to Baton Rouge, and down from the Ohio to Memphis.

But Memphis, although the Northern victory at the Battle of Corinth made her unnecessary as a fortress, had gunboats ready for action.

At six o'clock on a fine June morning, the people of Memphis crowded the bluff to watch the river. Colonel Ellet's four rams and five gunboats had steamed down from St. Louis and were lined up across the river opposite Memphis's eight gunboats. The firing began, back and forth, violently, the boats tilting like knights in a curious, clumsy, noisy, dangerous tournament to the death.

And by half past seven the people were going grimly and in silence back to their homes. The battle for Memphis was over. The city surrendered. And now the river was open as far as Vicksburg.

But since May 18, Vicksburg had had the North at bay. Vicksburg, on her great bluff above a loop in the river, was about halfway between Memphis and New Orleans. From neither direction could the Northern forces approach even within firing distance without getting in the way of the powerful batteries which raked the river with a murderous protection. The city was too high up on the hill for most gunboats and ironclads to be able to shoot effectively at such an extreme angle. There sat Vicksburg on her bluff, and all around, prowling like dogs trying to find a crack in a fence, ranged Grant's army and the Mississippi fleet.

Not until November, 1862, did Grant finally begin to worry about Vicksburg. He was having difficulties enough in keeping his supply lines open in the enemy's country. Around the rear of Vicksburg, General Pemberton had ranged a big army to defend the city, while the batteries covering the river took care of assault from that point. Up the Yazoo, curving northeast of Vicksburg, was the fort on Haines Bluff, guarded by twelve thousand men.

For a while, General Sherman thought he could slip in and take Haines Bluff by surprise, but as he came down the Mississippi with Davis's gunboat fleet, he was being watched all the way by Confederate spies in the swamps and on the hills . . . watching . . . following. They let Sherman push boldly up the Yazoo to Chickasaw Bayou. He left the boats there and set out on foot with his men on the precarious, swampy paths. Only a few of these were at all passable; all were commanded by the invisible sharpshooters on the bluffs. The battle was a short and deadly one. Sherman quickly retreated with his wounded.

Meanwhile, Grant spent two months of anguish and labor which came to exactly nothing. He wanted desperately to find a way to get past Vicksburg without going by river, as Pope's army had done when they neatly by-passed Island Number 10. So he started to cut a canal through the neck of the loop formed by the bend of the river opposite Vicksburg, a distance of less than a mile. But, since the canal would have to take big boats, it had to be more than sixty feet wide and more than nine feet deep. A dam was built across the upper end of Grant's Big Ditch, as it was scornfully called.

Night and day, dredges labored to deepen the canal. After six weeks, when the job seemed about finished, the river began to rise. It was March, and thaws up in the snow country were bringing down a spring freshet which broke the dam in a sudden crevasse and submerged the whole peninsula. Most of the horses were drowned, and the men had to run for their lives.

Grant next toyed with the idea of developing a channel through a series of rivers on the west shore which would take boats down a round-about way to join the Red River and then enter the Mississippi below Vicksburg, but abandoned that when he discovered Yazoo Pass. This was made to order.

Yazoo Pass formerly had been a canal leading out of the Mississippi, eastward, below Helena, Arkansas, to join the Coldwater River, then the Tallahatchie and the Yalobusha, to the Yazoo, and into the Mississippi again. This waterway would permit Grant to come in behind Haines Bluff. It was a by-pass which earlier had been in use by river men, until it was discovered that too much water was coming down into the lowlands from the Mississippi and actually threatening to divert the whole river in this direction. Yazoo Pass thereupon had been dammed and the channel no longer used.

General Grant dynamited the barrier. The water flowed down the old canal to meet the Coldwater River. It looked for a while as if the plan might work.

But the Confederates were not asleep. They had kept close watch on the activities up at Yazoo Pass. When the first gunboats pushed through the narrow waters, over which arched a dense bottomland forest, the Confederates were busily felling trees lower down across the Pass. At one stretch a mile long there were eighty great gums and water oaks and pecan trees tangled across the channel, and it took 500 Union soldiers two weary weeks to chop through, snake out the logs, and clear the way for the gunboats to join the Tallahatchie.

Then the 4,500 men on twenty-two steamboats, convoyed by several ironclads, set out to travel 250 miles through the swamps. The high water was in their favor, about the only thing that was. It not only put plenty of water in usually shallow streams and swamps, but made the terrain too mucky for sharpshooters to pick off the approaching fleet in the forest.

The Union boats sailed with some difficulty down the Tallahatchie. When they reached the point where the Yalobusha flows into it to form the Yazoo, they found a new Confederate earthwork fort bristling with guns, set on an Indian mound and barring the river. There was a fight which lasted for several days, but in the end the boats were more damaged than the fort on its ancient hillock.

The Union boats managed somehow to turn around in the river and steam disconsolately back again to Yazoo Pass and into the big open waters of the Mississippi. They were lucky that they had been in a wide enough river in which to turn around.

A little while later, another passageway through the swamp forests was discovered and hopefully followed . . . down the Big Sunflower River and into the Yazoo, only twenty miles above Haines Bluff. By following a network of waters—Steele's Bayou, Black Bayou, Deer Creek, Rolling Fork—they could make it. These streams were terribly narrow, however, and full of many twisting turns through a great cypress swamp.

Nevertheless, in March Sherman boldly went with small steamboats behind Porter's five ironclads and four mortar boats armed heavily with big guns, into Steele's Bayou. The boats nosed through the bushes, were entangled in wild grape vines and trumpet creepers; pilothouses and chimneys were knocked over. Birds fluttered wildly as the boats pushed through and broke off branches which cluttered the decks. There was a deafening clamor of squawks and screams as the fleet shoved through vast acres occupied by a heronry. Now and again a snake landed on deck, or a raccoon, knocked out of its tree, scrambled overboard to safety. Night and day, clouds of mosquitoes followed the boats and entered windows freely.

It was a most unlikely place to find steamboats, and certainly it was no place for gunboats fighting a war. The amazing thing is that they ever made their way in, and even more amazing that they got out.

Meanwhile, Confederate sharpshooters managed some good shots here and there, making life uncertain and doubly miserable, in addition to the trials of the wilderness. By the fifth day of this incredible swamp-safari, the ironclads had only contrived to advance thirty miles ahead of Sherman and his troops, when they suddenly met the enemy. At sight of them, the Confederate commander quickly ordered his men to fell trees across the creek in front of and behind the invading boats.

Sherman's scouts heard the racket. They hastened back to report the disaster. General Sherman located a narrow, soggy deer trail through the swamps, and, that night, he took his men through a wet, black wilderness, lighting their way with candles. In spite of the candles and the sloshing of many feet in the mud and water, they surprised the attackers and managed to drive them off.

But the Rolling Fork was blocked. The enemy had it tightly, and no one could pass. The boats would have to retreat, go back the way they came—*if* they could. So the dreadful, tangled tonnage of the barricade of trees was painfully removed from the rear. The creek, however, was much too narrow for boats to turn around in it. The ironclads, therefore, simply unshipped their rudders and backed out . . . clumsily, banging about from bank to bank, tangling in trees, roots, branches, vines.

Somehow, they got out of the aggravating little creek into which a fleet of gunboats and steamboats had been induced to travel. After eleven days of danger and swamp-struggling, the weary fleet arrived back in the Mississippi River, and doubtless Sherman, Porter and all the men heaved breaths of thankful relief to be on the deep water again!

And after all this great amount of effort and struggle, Grant was no nearer to Vicksburg than he had been before. Clearly, he could not take it from the rivers.

Next, therefore, he resolved on a bold and desperate plan, a win-all or lose-all game. He cut his line of land communications. He traveled light, with few supplies, and boldly approached Vicksburg overland, from behind. He fought Pemberton's army and Johnston's army separately, but conclusively, and suddenly found himself where he had tried to be for months. He was close enough to Vicksburg to demand a surrender.

Pemberton, however, retreated to the city. He preferred a

siege to flight. For six weeks, Grant battered Vicksburg. His gunboats now came boldly into the river below the bluff and tossed in shell after shell.

The people of Vicksburg held out for a long time. They lived in caves, out of danger, but when food grew scarce and more costly, then General Pemberton knew he would have to surrender or the city would starve.

On July 4, 1863, when Gettysburg was also a Northern victory, the beautiful city on the bluffs, the Gibraltar of the Mississippi, in desolation surrendered. With the fort at Grand Gulf yielded earlier, and Port Hudson having surrendered, and with Vicksburg taken at last, the Mississippi was free again, free from her source to her outlet in the sea.

CHAPTER SEVENTEEN

1874: " . . architects who build
The bridges o'er swift rivers and abysses
Before impassable to human feet."
LONGFELLOW

IT was bad enough, steamboat men averred, when the Rock Island Railroad built the first bridge across the Mississippi in 1856, connecting Rock Island, Illinois, with Davenport, Iowa. Boat after boat was wrecked on the bridge piers, among the first such obstructions to get in the way of free navigation on the whole long length of the Mississippi. To river pilots, the bridge was known as "Hellgate," and the "invention of Satan and the Rock Island Railroad." But when plans were afoot to put a bridge across the Mississippi at St. Louis, the steamboat men had worse comments to make than they had ever thought up about the upper-river span.

It was, besides, a very different sort of river at St. Louis, above which the bulk of the Missouri swelled the Mississippi. The river galloped at such a speed and depth here that no one believed that bridge piers could be erected. Even if they should be put up, it was doubted that they would stand for long. The river would scour out the mud around them and topple them into the water.

Not even the architectural engineers of the mid-nineteenth century believed that such piers could be successful. None had been before in the most wildly rushing rivers of the world. These engineers proved their point by showing how any obstruction standing in swift water, be it stick or rock or bridge pier, causes the water to surge more rapidly around it, setting up an eddy which churns and swirls and digs out the bottom deeper around the obstruction.

To build a bridge at St. Louis was believed to be impossible. So Captain James B. Eads—tall, dynamic, forceful James Eads, river expert—set about doing it. Of all his amazing accomplishments in improving the Mississippi, perhaps he is best known for his bridge.

Today it is called the Eads Bridge. In the past, however, it was most often known as *The Bridge*. Not *a* bridge; this was something special. Until it was built, all railroads in Illinois and Missouri had had to transfer freight and passengers to ferries, to be transported slowly and with a good deal of effort across the river. A bridge was a vital need, so, in spite of lawsuits, objections, doubts and difficulty in obtaining the money, the way finally was cleared, and Eads eagerly set to work to build The Bridge.

Four great foundations would be all that would support the tips of three great steel arches. The two middle piers would be 520 feet apart, the other two 502 feet in each direction toward the shores. Three of these foundation piers would be sunk to the bedrock itself, while the fourth, near the east bank where the rock lay extraordinarily deep, would be set upon metal pilings driven down to it. The arches of the bridge, longer than any ever known, would be of steel, which had not been used in bridge building before. The east abutment would go down 120 feet to reach bedrock, the height of a ten-story building. To cope with the savagery of the Mississippi and perform a job as it never was done earlier, Eads had to design new machinery—sand pumps, compressed air chambers, strange engines—and he had to insist upon extremely high standards of excellence for his steel and iron.

One shocked look at his plans sent many people hurriedly to tell Eads that steel arches more than five hundred feet long, with only their tips resting on the piers, would surely collapse of their own weight. Besides, said many, getting the foundations down to bedrock was foolhardy; anyway, those piers would crumble before anyone set foot on them.

Work, however, went ahead in 1867 with the building of the cofferdam. This was two great cylinders of heavy sheet piling, one smaller than the other, with a space of six feet between them, as two boxes would be nested one inside the other. The space between the cylinders was packed with clay. Then the water was pumped out of the interior so that the bottom of the river was revealed and the pumps and pile drivers could get to work on the mud. They had to penetrate through this to bedrock, and the rock was a long way down.

As the pile drivers and pumps labored, they ran into a remarkable collection of curios which held no delight to the workmen. They were boring down through an assortment of sunken steamboats and steam boilers and much other cast-off or lost materials of the civilization which was St. Louis. A great deal of valuable time had to be devoted to breaking through this massive junk and getting it out of the cofferdam. When they thought everything was out, they discovered the remains of still another derelict steamboat! Meanwhile, the cofferdam sprung leaks. They were patiently plugged and patched.

The leaks solved, the caisson was begun for the west pier, standing in the river. Eads' pneumatic caissons had never been used before in bridge building. They were great elliptical bells, eighty-two feet high, which were open at the bottom. They were made of wood and covered with sheet iron. For the west pier, the caisson was forty-eight feet wide, but for the east pier it was sixty feet in width. The bottomless air chamber, nine feet high, formed the lower part. The sandy bed of the river would be its floor until this was pumped out and the caisson rested at last on bedrock While it was sinking, compressed air was pumped in so that the caisson could withstand the extremely heavy pressure of the river all around it. Upon its roof the stout, hollow masonry foundations would be built and filled with concrete.

Down in the caisson on the river's bottom, the men labored on short shifts, for the pressure was difficult to endure. Some became ill and suffered a form of paralysis called the "bends," later known as Caisson Disease.

James Eads, from his years of diving experience and salvage operations in the Mississippi, knew what pressure was like far down in the river. He visited the pressure chamber daily and watched the men. When they became ill, they were removed, and the others were put on shorter hours and special diets. Day and night, men worked in shifts, and the great stone column of the pier was rising inside the chamber.

February 28, 1870, and the east pier caisson reached bedrock, ninety-three and one-half feet under water. The men set to work to fill the air chamber with stone and brick, the stairs were removed, and the filling of the last opening began. Then the river began to rise, deepening the water over the caisson, increasing the pressure unbearably, so that the "bends" hit the men again. Some days later, a man died many hours after he came to the surface. Several more deaths occurred, and James Eads, in grief and desperation, cut the working hours even more.

In April, another flood battered the construction until the east pier caisson was damaged so badly that it sprung a leak, the sheet iron was ruptured, and the inner stairway was cut off. A month of repair lay ahead . . . always delays, Eads groaned. But when that was finished, the pier was soon completed, and it was time to build the heavy masonry tower. Almost at the same time, the west pier reached the bottom—bedrock— seventy-eight feet down.

Christmas, 1870 . . . an ice gorge of massive extent threatened to crush the breakwaters . . . March 8, 1871, a tornado struck St. Louis and wrecked the waterfront, smashed the east abutment frames . . . sent tons of heavy timbers crashing down on air pumps and hoses, on hydraulic lifts and air pipes . . killed one man, injured eight. But three weeks later the frames were up again, and indomitably the work continued. The endless courage and encouragement of James Eads pushed the men to almost superhuman feats of labor.

Four great foundations and their completed towers finally stood tall above the surging Mississippi, where engineers had been so sure no piers could stand. They were isolated islands, unconnected as yet with land.

The Bridge now required the best steel, and steel manufacture in those days was not as expert nor as excellent as it was later to be. It was difficult to find the men and material to produce the quality of steel on which Eads insisted. The first steel bridge in the world had to be perfect, strong enough to last hundreds of years. His orders for steel and parts were tremendous, and Eads' standards were so high and so rigid that it was six months before the chosen steel plant turned out a single stave which met his requirements—and he needed more than six thousand just like it!

1871–1872 . . . produce that steel, produce that steel, produce that steel . . . no, not like that, like *this*, all of them like *this!* . . . delays, delays, delays. And tall James Eads was fuming and pacing, then hurrying east to the steel mills to speed things along, forcing his high standards, insisting only on the best . . . and finally getting it.

1873 . . . the arches began to grow toward each other from the piers, would meet over the river, midway of the span. The difficult problem of cantilevering a bridge of this size had never been solved before, and there was the usual flurry of distrust and lack of faith across the country, while the steel arches continued to creep closer to each other.

They would meet any day, now. But the weather was blistering hot, as the Mississippi Valley so well knows how to produce it. The steel, measured exactly, must come together exactly . . . but the heat had caused it to expand just enough so that the pieces would not fit. James Eads paced. Then he ordered ice, tons of ice, ice in gunny sacks applied to the summer-hot steel, day and night, to cause that needful contraction which would bring the pieces together. And the pieces met. . . .

September 17, 1873 . . . and the first span was completed. By the end of October, with cooler weather, the arches all but spanned the river.

Money was running short. As if this were not problem enough, a fiery lawsuit arose, instigated by irate steamboat men who claimed the bridge was too low and would be a menace to navigation, just as they had fumed at Davenport and Burlington and Minneapolis. When Eads brushed them aside, they petitioned President Grant to have The Bridge torn down. Eads laughed. But the situation was grave, and he only laughed because to tear down The Bridge now would be like tearing down the city of St. Louis itself, or the National Capitol, or Niagara Falls. The Bridge would stand long after steamboats were gone.

President Grant wrathily refused to listen to the petitioners. The Bridge was safe.

Sunday, May 24, 1874. The sidewalks across The Bridge were open. People in their Sunday best . . . ladies, gentlemen, children, rivermen, roustabouts . . . walked almost hesitantly, and somewhat reverently, across their bridge. The view was wonderful from up there, up and down the river, far across into Illinois to the far bluffs, and to the city of St. Louis, proudly sitting beside her river and her Bridge. The day was inexpressibly fine, and The Bridge was the greatest thing they had ever experienced. The whole city felt a curious glow of personal elation at the sight of the triumphant structure standing there, calmly reaching across the once unspannable Mississippi.

At 5:30 o'clock in the morning of June 3, four fine horses, hitched to the heaviest coal wagon in St. Louis, were waiting on the St. Louis side of The Bridge, to be the first to cross as it was opened. Behind the coal wagon and its thundering horses came brewery wagons and private carriages, delivery wagons and open barouches, men on horseback and peddlers' carts, as one and all tried out the strength of The Bridge. If it would hold all these . . . but it hadn't tried a railroad train, warned the hard-to-convince skeptics . . . a railroad train is mighty heavy!

July 2 . . . people crowded the banks. Fourteen big locomotives, their tenders filled with water and coal, and with people clinging recklessly to everything they could hold on to, blew their whistles, got up steam, and thundered across The Bridge. They crossed and recrossed, testing it to its utmost. First seven locomotives went over. They paused dramatically at each pier top. Then fourteen went, seven on each track, crossing side by side. Finally, the fourteen went over in a single impressive procession, steaming and thundering and with their whistles screaming their triumph. And The Bridge did not even quiver.

The yelling and shouting on the shores and the hooting of steamboat whistles from boats gathered below The Bridge crowded out even the huffing and puffing of the locomotives.

Independence Day, 1874. This was it! All St Louis turned out. There were parades and floats and costumes and carriages and people. There were six hundred members of German singing societies, vigorously performing the joyfully endless verses of the *Schnitzelbank*, to the edification of the populace. The fire department, the police department, cavalry from Jefferson Barracks . . . they all paraded under a triumphal arch near the opening of The Bridge, and went across, solemnly yet gaily, to the other side, and then back again, while the Mississippi flowed on below. It surged around the massive piers which had cost the lives of men, as it had flowed before there was a bridge.

At the celebration in his honor, later in the day, James Eads said:

"The bridge . . . stands forth, not as the result of one man's talents, but as the crystallized thought of many minds, and as the enduring evidence of toil of many hands."

St. Louisans had a motto for a long time:

"The Mississippi, discovered by Marquette, 1673
Spanned by Captain Eads, 1874."

And the breath of a wind moved over the night, and sang a curious melody through the black steel lace of the bridge James Eads had built.

CHAPTER EIGHTEEN

1879: "Man puts his hand to the flinty rock
and overturns mountains by the roots.
He cuts a channel in the rocks, and his
eye sees every precious thing.
He binds up the streams so that they do not trickle,
And the thing that is hid he brings forth to light.
BOOK OF JOB

IT was an enormous job: control the entire length of the Mississippi; insist that all 2,552 miles of an unruly river conform; keep it within its prescribed banks; maintain a safe, well-lighted, well-marked, nine-foot channel all the way to the head of navigation. Tell that river that it must not eat out its curves nor make unexpected cut-offs; that it must flow properly and carry thousands of boats and millions of tons of cargo from the Gulf of Mexico to Minneapolis every year. For mere man to expect all this and to actually control a river like the Mississippi, is a little like demanding that he should control the tides, tell the wind when to stop blowing, or remodel the Rocky Mountains.

On the day before the Battle of Bunker Hill, in 1775, the very first indirect seeds of Mississippi management began when a Corps of Engineers was hastily organized to assist General Washington's army. The Corps was somewhat increased in numbers later that year by Washington himself, to build bridges, erect earthworks and cut roads. Because engineers of this calibre were scarce in the Colonies, Washington hurriedly called for French officers, who taught the young recruits of the Corps. It was a long time after this, however, before the United States Corps of Engineers paid any attention to the Mississippi River, out in the western wilderness.

As a basically wartime group, dedicated to getting an army to where it must go, the Engineers Corps in peacetime found itself without a job. Then it was given the perpetual nonmilitary commission of creating and maintaining river and harbor improvements. The great harbors of the American coastline were built by the Corps of Engineers. Not until 1825, however, did any work begin on that wild monster of a Mississippi which no man had tried to control before.

The first work on the big river was the result of a contract with a civilian, Captain Henry M. Shreve, to cut out the snags in the Mississippi. After some difficulty, Shreve's new kind of snagboat set out to remove the menace of the snags and did it thoroughly. In later years, the Engineers, with bigger snagboats, continued the unending job of Toothpullers of the River.

After this successful operation, the Mississippi was pretty much let alone, except for extensive work which was done by Lieutenant Robert E. Lee, to save the St. Louis harbor and to remove the menace of the Des Moines Rapids, above Keokuk. The problem of the silting ship channels at the mouth of the

Mississippi came in for some rather futile harrowing and dredging. Then came the War between the States, and river work ended.

It was those hostilities, however, which revealed more plainly than dozens of complaints from steamboat captains how very much needed to be done to make the Mississippi properly navigable. Irate Admiral Farragut had had his big ships embarrassingly stuck for days before they could get over the mud bar and up to capture New Orleans. Supply boats had been stranded on sand bars, and the river, it was discovered, had sprouted a whole new crop of snags.

Opening the mouth of the stream was a job of primary importance, for New Orleans was about to lose her foreign trade. Ocean ships were finding it more and more difficult to come up the river to the city's harbor.

The Engineers toyed with the idea of cutting a canal from New Orleans to the Gulf; they tried dredging and plowing the accumulations at the mouth. Nothing worked for long. When Captain Eads presented his plan of building jetties, it took a long time to convince the authorities that it would work.

Upstream, Captain Eads explained, a dredge could dig out the bottom muck and dispose of it, leaving a fairly stable channel. This was because the Mississippi, in coming down that continental slant, was scouring out the channel with the force of its own current. Down at sea level the rush was over, the energy spent. The Mississippi oozed languidly to the sea. And the silt which had been held in suspension for hundreds or for thousands of miles, promptly settled to the bottom. When dredged out, it simply filled in again.

The solution presented by Eads was this: put something solid along the edges of the Mississippi as it went to meet the Gulf, so that the water would have to push past, not ease along, and it would dig out a channel for itself, deep enough for any ship.

Work began. From barges and boats, great poles and pilings were driven deeply into the mud, making a wall on either side of Southwest Pass. Crews of men cut thousands of willows to weave into a "mattress," which was shoved into place between the pilings. Even before this wall was finished, the channel was visibly deepening. In a short while, it was twenty feet deep, and ocean ships confidently came up to New Orleans. The Corps of Engineers soon afterward took over the job of maintaining a minimum depth of thirty-five feet all the way up to Baton Rouge.

Taming a river like the Mississippi was a new sort of problem for which previous experience on other jobs was of little use. The Mississippi was a rule unto itself. When this was realized, the Mississippi River Commission was formed, in 1879, as a separate body, devoting all its time to that river, to build its bridges, remove its wrecks, dredge its channel, build levees, erect dikes and wing-dams to protect shores, and, with the assistance of the U.S. Coast Guard, to mark it with lights and buoys.

Samuel Clemens, an old riverman who thought he knew everything about the Mississippi because he had spent a good deal of time as a pilot on that stream before the War between the States, had little confidence in what the Engineers and Coast Guard were doing. Very likely many rivermen of his time echoed his sentiments. He wrote:

"The military engineers of the U.S. River Commission have taken upon their shoulders the job of making the Mississippi over again—a job transcended in size by only the original job of creating it. One who knows the Mississippi will promptly aver—not aloud, but to himself—that ten thousand River Commissions, with the mines of the world at their backs, cannot tame that lawless stream, cannot curb it or confine it, cannot say to it, Go here, or Go there, and make it obey, cannot save a shore which it has sentenced; cannot bar its path with an obstruction which it will not tear down, dance over, and laugh at . . . One would pipe out and say the Commission might as well bully the comets in their courses and undertake to make them behave, as try to bully the Mississippi into right and reasonable conduct."

But somehow these men did a good deal of what they set out to do, though the job is one which is never finished. Again carped critic Clemens:

"When there used to be four thousand steamboats and ten thousand acres of coal barges and rafts, and trading scows, there wasn't a lantern from St. Paul to New Orleans, and the snags were thicker than bristles on a hog's back; and now, where there's three dozen steamboats and nary a barge or raft, Government has snatched out all the snags and lit up the shores like Broadway, and a boat's as safe on the river as she'd be in heaven. And I reckon that by the time there aren't any boats left at all, the Commission will have the old thing all reorganized and dredged out and fenced in, and tidied up, to a degree that will make navigation just simply perfect, and absolutely safe and profitable."

In part, the criticism was true: the steamboats appeared to be vanishing from the rivers. Men and cities, for a while, turned their backs on the Mississippi. Yet, without that century of planning, directing, cajoling, lighting, marking and remodeling of the Mississippi, it would not have been navigable by the middle 1920's, when the Age of Diesel Towboats began to replace the remaining steamboats. The latter, however, never entirely vanished. One of the last, the old *Fort Gage*, burned at St. Louis, in 1956. The *Ste. Genevieve*, a large side-wheeler, ferries freight trains across the Mississippi. Several modern steamboats are used as towboats, and the *Delta Queen* is a fine steamboat, carrying passengers on the Ohio and the Mississippi.

The Diesel boats, operated with powerful screw propellers and with the engine invented by Rudolph Diesel, fueled with the low-priced oil which also bears his name, travel with a good deal more security, freedom and safety than any steamboat pilot in the old days ever knew.

Indispensable guides to the Mississippi are the books of maps which have been made and are kept up to date by the Corps, who, as Topographical Engineers, try to follow the river's changes. With these charts, a navigator on the biggest towboat or the smallest cruiser may travel from Minneapolis to New Orleans and the mouth of the Mississippi and be fairly sure of his channel, its depth, shore installations and scenic and historic points.*

After many years during which nothing was done about flood control by the Engineers or anyone else, the problem was taken on as a permanent job of the Corps. To keep the Mississippi inside its banks and consequently tend to deepen it, the Engineers have built levees wherever needed above the mouth of the Ohio, and they have almost completely walled the river with grass-sodded earthen levees or revetments, faced with stone, asphalt, or concrete. This latter type of levee is used where the current or eddies eat into the soft banks. Most of the river walls on the lower Mississippi are of this sort. And it is appalling to any Engineer or civilian to observe the force of a grinding eddy eating out a four-inch-thick layer of asphalt on a revetment which is breaking apart like a graham cracker and sliding into the brown water!

Yet the river is just as quick to desert a revetment as it is to eat it up. When the Mississippi chooses to get out of its bed and make a new one in the far cornfields, or cuts off a loop, it may leave miles of expensive revetments high and dry, off in a rural landscape far from the water.

Those cut-offs have always been a part of the nature of the Mississippi as well as a headache to the Engineers and navigators, and they have played havoc with state boundaries. As the river swings its big loops, the water tends to gnaw into the inner curves and finally breaks through The outer curves are left as ox-bow lakes, which eventually dry up or become swamps. The river flows straighter for a little way, until it swings again in more loops. Sometimes, however, a cut-off is desirable to shorten distance and speed flood water on its way, so, between the years

* For information on obtaining river maps, write to the U.S Corps of Engineers, 420 Locust Street, St. Louis 21, Missouri.

1929 and 1942, the Engineers made sixteen cut-offs, which shortened the river 151.8 miles.

This sidewinder-habit of sliding laterally from one side of its vast basin to the other has necessitated a continuous battle to keep the river where it belongs—or where people think it belongs. A city built on a river expects to stay there; but there are those like Vicksburg, Greenville, and Arkansas City which have been neatly by-passed by the river, leaving them inland or on chutes but little connected with the main body of the Mississippi. In other instances, especially in the past, when the Engineers were not on the job, the river simply ate up such towns as Napoleon, Arkansas, Prentiss, Mississippi, and Kaskaskia, Illinois, and many another hopeful village set unwisely beside the great and hungry waters.

Save the banks, control floods, maintain and protect channels; these three are perhaps the main jobs entrusted to the Engineers today. From the standpoint of the navigator, the latter is most important. To be navigable to today's big boats, the channel must be at least nine feet deep and three hundred feet wide. The deep-water channel is kept at a thirty-five-foot minimum and five-hundred-foot width, from the Gulf to Baton Rouge. Keeping the rest of the river, all the way to Minneapolis, dredged out to a nine-foot depth is an endless problem during the years of drouth which often afflict America and the Mississippi Valley.

In addition, in certain stretches of the upper river the channel route has been dynamited through solid rock, so that dredging is of little help during low water. In the past, the upper river was notable for its shallowness in summer, when most of the water once seemed to drain away and leave nothing much for a boat to float in. In the dry summer of 1936, the upper river was only four feet deep and navigation ended above Dubuque, Iowa, until the autumn rains at last put water back into the greatest river in North America.

The trouble lies in the difference in altitude of some 1,475 feet between the headwaters of the Mississippi, at Lake Itasca in Minnesota, and the slow, lazy finish of the river in marshes along the Gulf of Mexico. Just between the head of navigation at St. Anthony's Falls and the mouth of the Missouri above St. Louis, the Mississippi pours down a continental slope of 324 feet, spread out over 658 miles. Either the current was raging in high water, or else it drained down too fast and left a river one could wade across in summertime.

Not until the Engineers, in the '30's, built the "Mississippi Stairway" of locks and dams and turned the river into a canal, in order to control the water level and maintain a nine-foot channel, did the upper Mississippi become reliably navigable.

The steps in this tremendous staircase, at this writing, are composed of twenty-seven locks and twenty-six dams. The dams hold back the water, create broad lakes above themselves and maintain a sustained water supply and navigation channel. The locks permit boats to pass around the dams and climb or descend from level to level. Lock and Dam Number 1 are located at St. Paul, Minnesota. Lock and Dam Number 26 are at Alton, Illinois. The others are spaced between, with an average of about twenty-five miles between them.

For many years this was the total of locks and dams on the river stairway, but today, eighteen miles downriver from Alton Lock, there is the new Chain of Rocks canal, where Lock Number 27 is put into use to eliminate the hazards of the old Chain of Rocks area, near St. Louis. This is the stretch in which many a steamboat tore herself to pieces in the old days, and where the Indians felt there was a demon to devour them. It has been proposed to build a dam near Chain of Rocks bridge, and to put another a few miles below St. Louis, to deepen the city's harbor.

One by one, within a decade, the locks and dams were completed. At Dubuque, Iowa, on a hot day in August, 1938, a pretty young lady dedicated Number 11.

"I christen thee the General Pike Lock and Dam!" cried the

young Centennial Queen, smashing a ribbon-wrapped bottle on the railing of the new dam . . . named for that same Pike who, as a youthful, adventurous, red-haired lieutenant, came in 1805 in search of the river's source. He was the first man wearing the uniform of the United States Army to set foot on that spot

Water from the broken bottle splashed into the Mississippi River and mingled with it—salt water from the Atlantic and the Pacific, brought by Captain Richard Bissell, river captain and author, from a world cruise. A thirteen-gun salute crashed from the howitzers of the 80th Field Artillery, in honor of Major General Schley, Chief of the Army Engineers, who was present, and the lock gates slowly opened. First to enter was the *Ellen*, a steamboat in the government service. Following her came the *Mark Twain* with a loaded tow of barges, and then a triumphant parade of boats proceeded through the locks.

Two years later, the last link in the Mississippi's canalization, Clarksville Lock and Dam, Number 25, a few miles above Number 26 at Alton, was finished. The upper Mississippi was ready, with its controlled channel, for the great surge of northbound and southbound traffic—towboats shoving wheat and soybeans out of Minneapolis and gasoline, molasses, fuel oil and coal from lower river ports, endlessly passing and repassing on the river.

Guiding them on the protected channel are the shore lights and buoys set by the Coast Guard—red, conical nun buoys marking the east side, black and white can buoys marking the west (or the right and left, upbound). In winter, the Coast Guard ice-breakers clear a way for busy boats. Night and day, the river is guarded by its government protectors.

One of the most recent, vital and dangerous problems to confront the Engineers is that of the Atchafalaya River. It is connected with the Mississippi River, ninety miles below Natchez, by several miles of Old River. Where Old River and the Red come together, the Atchafalaya is born.

Evidently at some time during the Pleistocene, the Mississippi turned to the right at Old River and took the Atchafalaya route, to empty into the Gulf, instead of down its present channel past Baton Rouge and New Orleans. Right now, at Old River entry, the Mississippi has been insidiously inching in again, has been sending more and more water in that direction. The Corps of Engineers began noticing this tendency some time ago and immediately set about planning for a solution to the problem. Yearly, meanwhile, it has grown more alarming.

The Mississippi shows every indication of wanting to desert its present course. This tragedy would leave New Orleans upon a salt-water estuary—a dismal stream depriving the old city of fresh water for homes and industry and prohibiting river and sea traffic from coming to its great port and to that of Baton Rouge. A lock must be built across the entry into Old River before a rambunctious surge of water turns its massive channel and decides to go via the Atchafalaya to the Gulf again. And if it does so, it will take more than the United States Government and the Corps of Engineers to stop it!

In spite of new worries and old problems, the Corps of Engineers and the Coast Guard have, as much as any men can, tamed and remodeled the Mississippi. Their job is never done As long as the Mississippi continues to flow down a continent, these men will have fresh problems to solve.

CHAPTER NINETEEN

1937: *"All the fountains of the great deep burst forth
and the windows of the heavens were opened . . .
And rain fell upon the earth."*

BOOK OF GENESIS

IT had been raining for days in Ohio. Raining in West Virginia.
Raining in Pennsylvania. It was pouring in Illinois, in Missouri,
in Indiana; in Kentucky, in Arkansas, in Tennessee. It was January, 1937, and out of the Caribbean Sea a warm, tropical, low-
pressure atmosphere, laden with moisture, had moved unaccountably northwest, where it had no business to be in January. There
it met a blast of polar air shoving down over the snows of Wisconsin, Minnesota and Canada. On impact with the cold air, the
Bermuda moisture in the atmosphere condensed as rain. Lots of
rain. Consequently the southern states were unseasonably warm

and unreasonably wet, while the Ohio and Mississippi Valleys had prolonged heavy downpours which soon saturated the soggy January earth. The result was not only heavy rain and mud, it was disaster.

Water came down in torrents. The Midwest, endlessly deluged from a low gray sky, turned into a muddy mess Streets ran water to the curbs; sewers overflowed and backed up. People complained of flooded basements. Fields began to show large lakes; earth roads were bottomless.

And in Ohio, the Miami River was rising. All the little creeks and rivulets were full and were pouring muddy water into it. The Scioto was rising. The Muskingum was rising, and so was the Hocking in its deep valley with all its heavy run-off. So was Mill Creek, insignificant little Mill Creek at Cincinnati.

In Pennsylvania, the mountains shed the winter rains faster than they would have shed them in the growing time, when crops and grass and trees would soak up much extra moisture. The little mountain runs were galloping full, emptying into the Allegheny and the Youghiogheny, into the Conemaugh and into the Shenango, emptying into the Monongahela in its narrow valley through the coal-mine hills. These rivers in turn were dumping their load into the Ohio, which was climbing higher by the hour.

Down in West Virginia, the Kanawha and the Little Kanawha were coming up fast. In Kentucky, the Cumberland was out of its banks and the people in Pineville, deep in a narrow gorge, were leaving their riverside houses and taking to the hills. The Rolling Fork was rushing full of muddy water. The Kentucky River was a solid yellow torrent, pounding past the sheer bluffs, spreading out over the level lands where Dan Boone had built Boonesborough so long ago. The Green River was flooding in the cave country; parts of Mammoth Cave were under water. The Tennessee was coming up into Nashville's streets. Little Knob Creek, fed by the big run-off in the hills, was over the road through Knob Creek Valley, where the Lincolns used to live.

Troublesome Creek was getting out of hand, and so were the Licking and the Tradewater. And still it rained.

It was the same thing in Indiana. The overly full White River spread into the winter fields, and the Patoka and the Tippecanoe, the Little Pigeon River and the Wabash—the Wabash had a broken levee and was all over the Vincennes bottoms, drowning out the stubble and was spreading wider . . . wider . . .

Over in Illinois, the Little Wabash was adding its bit, and so were the Bonpas and the Embarrass and Skillet Fork, and the Big Muddy and the Little Muddy, living up to their names, and the Cache—watch out for the Cache, said the people of Cairo, there in that touchy spot where the Ohio and the Mississippi meet. Watch out for the Cache! Watch out for Cairo!

By mid-January, the sea wall at Portsmouth, Ohio, broke and much of Portsmouth was under water. Mill Creek at Cincinnati was running wild. A sixth of that entire city was deeply flooded. Eight square miles of Paducah were inundated. Half of Evansville was flooded; a large part of Louisville was desperately in need of rescue. The Red Cross took over. Rescue crews commandeered all the boats available, took people off rooftops, saved families from upstairs rooms, paddled boats through the downstairs, searching for what they hoped they would not find. A devastating fire broke out on the Cincinnati waterfront, when oil tanks broke under water pressure. The Ohio's flood crest had risen ten feet higher than at any other known time in history.

When the main crest had been reached, and when a cold wave stopped the rain and turned it to snow in the upper valley, it seemed as if the worst was over. But Cairo, down at that junction of the two rivers, was waiting for what was coming.

For when the waters upstream began to recede, there was only one place for them to go—down that continental slant by way of the Big Ditch, the great drainage system of the Ohio and the Mississippi.

Sixty billion tons of water had fallen in the Valley. Add that to the normal bulk of two great rivers, and you have a monster raging down the slope toward the sea. Before the flood crest reached Cairo, it had inundated ninety-four cities and towns, had cut off their water supplies, had rendered a million people homeless. All this, before Cairo.

Cairo, Illinois, lies on a triangular point of low land, at the junction of the Ohio with the Mississippi. Cairo's levees must protect two sides of that triangle, must resist tremendous pressure from two flooding rivers, with a flood wall on the north keeping out the Cache which empties into the Ohio a few miles above the city. Now the Cache was threatening to burst the flood gates at the rear of Cairo.

But Cairo believed in the strength of its levees, and in that fairly new "escape valve," a little way down the Mississippi. The Birds Point-New Madrid Floodway could be opened at strategic points to permit the river to spread out over miles of bottom-land, away from cities. It would flood thousands of acres of farm-land and forest, but that was better, the Engineers figured, than allowing all that water pressure to burst levees along cities and endanger human lives.

The Floodway below Cairo was guarded by a levee which would be blasted with dynamite when the pressure grew too great on the levees at Cairo. Five miles back of the Floodway levee another earth wall had been built to prevent the water from spreading too far inland. Farmers in the area, however, were not pleased with the prospect before them.

When the Engineers finally went to dynamite the levee and release waters through the Floodway, they met farmers with shotguns, armed men muddy to their waists, grimly standing on a levee whose top was only a little way out of the menacing waters.

"Over our dead bodies!" they declared and leveled their guns. But that levee had to be opened. The objectors had to stand aside. The National Guard of Missouri was sent to protect the men delegated to set off the charge.

Tons of earth blew skyward. A great crevasse burst apart and the Mississippi, like a tidal wave, surged through. Seventy-five miles long and five miles wide, the water spread. For a while the menace to Cairo was lessened. But it was only for a little while, for the spillway itself was filling up, and there still seemed to be no end to the water which was coming down the Ohio and the Mississippi. Women and children and the old and ill were sent out of Cairo; only able-bodied men remained to guard the levees and continue desperately building them higher. The levees soon were raised to withstand sixty feet of water, but the Engineers insisted they must be built even higher, at least two feet more, because the river was still coming up.

Down in the streets of Cairo, far below the river level, one could see the tilted roofs of floating barns and houses going by on the flood, and trees wallowing along.

In the past few years of flood control, the Engineers had built a billion dollars' worth of strong levees along the Mississippi, from Cairo to New Orleans, and the time had surely come which was to test them. If they broke—if the greatest flood in the history of the river burst through those levees, land fifty miles wide on either side of the Mississippi would be flooded. In this eventuality, the Army made large-scale plans to evacuate a million people from the threatened valley . . . if the levees broke . . . if the levees broke . . .

Meanwhile, up at Cairo, it was getting worse by the minute. The strain on the watchers was intense. On the other side of the levee, the Ohio was going by on a level with the street lights. The wall was raised higher once more. Sandboils started at the north end of the city. Streams of water gushed in under the pressure of the tremendous rivers rushing by outside. The pumps worked night and day, tossing back the muddy water as fast as it came in.

For twelve miles of menaced levee wall the men toiled and watched. And if that wall began to go, the Engineers were to let in the water as slowly as possible, so that, as sirens and bells and whistles blared the warning of total evacuation, men would have time to get out and the city would not be completely ruined by a mountainous gush of water.

Waves were lapping, under a wind, at the top of the Cairo levee. Downstream, the town of Hickman, Kentucky, was in extreme danger as its own levee weakened. A hundred thousand sandbags were hauled in a hurry to Tiptonville, to mend the Reelfoot Lake levee. At Memphis, the river was three miles wide and climbing alarmingly up the levee. And, if all those sixty billion extra tons of water and debris shoving down the Mississippi descended upon New Orleans, its own long-tested levees would surely burst. But only two years before, the Engineers had built another escape valve, the Bonnet Carré spillway, twenty-eight miles above New Orleans.

At this point, in flood after flood, for hundreds of years, the river had burst over its banks or broken through levees, and washed down into Lake Pontchartrain, five miles away, devastating the plantations which lay in its path. If the Mississippi wanted to get through there so badly, it must be a natural spillway.

The Engineers therefore, at tremendous expense, built a great concrete spillway and cleared a broad floodway. When the big waters came crowding down that thousand-mile stretch of Mississippi between the Ohio and the Gulf, the Bonnet Carré spillway was opened, a gate at a time, until 250,000 cubic feet of muddy water a second were pouring through, tumultuously but safely, on the way to Lake Pontchartrain and the Gulf. New Orleans was safe.

Yes, the escape-valves were working. The billion-dollar line of levees held. Cairo, New Orleans and the cities between were safe!

That was the Big Flood. It was indeed the largest which historical times have recorded. From that earliest noted inundation which the Gentleman of Elvas mentioned in his journal of De Soto's expedition along the Mississippi, until the flood in

1937, none were known to have been greater than the latter.

Engineers, however, remember the 1937 flood, when twenty inches of rain came down in two weeks' time, and they know what those sixty billion tons of water did to the two valleys. They also know that a similar combination of weather factors may easily occur again—a warm, tropical, low-pressure area pushing up unseasonably from Bermuda, and a cold, high-pressure area shoving down from the polar regions, over the northern snow country, to meet the warm air . . . and they know that tremendous rains result. It was only a whim, perhaps, that in 1937 the deluge stopped at twenty inches. It could have been more.

The Engineers realize that it could have been much more. The people of the flooded cities perhaps know it, too. They understand that, although everyone thinks, "It can never happen like that again," the same situation may easily come to pass this year or next year or the year after. Then the Mississippi River may rampage down its huge valley in the greatest flood which mankind has ever known. For the Mississippi is that kind of river . . . unpredictable even when it is apparently foreseeable . . . ferocious when it is apparently docile. The river . . . the river . . . always the river. . . .

CHAPTER TWENTY

"A King among the rivers! On thy way
A hundred towns await and welcome thee—"
LONGFELLOW

RIVER towns are not like other places. They have drunk up and have absorbed some of the quality of the river, have become part of its indelible character, reflect the personalities of the people who built them. Just as the Mississippi itself is different, from its upper reaches to its lower, so do the towns differ, one from the other, according to the kind of water washing their doorsteps and the kinds of circumstances surrounding their creation.

Towns along the upper Mississippi are closely a part of the river. They are built on its shores; their streets come in friendly fashion down to the water front. A passing boat may look up one street after another, and see the bright lights of Saturday night, see the laundry hung out to dry on Monday, see children going to school and the business of the town along Main Street. People wave at the boats or flash lights at night to signal a friendly greeting.

On the lower Mississippi, the situation is very different. This section of the river is broad and dangerous. Here, either the towns are high on the bluffs, or they seem to crouch behind the levee, far below the level of the water, so that only the roof-tops and the arching crowns of trees are visible from the river. These towns, though very much influenced by the river, do not seem to be as intimately a part of it as the upper settlements are.

There were so many reasons for building a town along the Mississippi, yet they all go back to the basic reason for building a place of habitation anywhere—a spot where its people may make a living. Since the river primarily was a highway of commerce and travel, the only long route through the middlewestern wilderness—a land largely without roads of any kind—the cities and towns and villages, the forts and landings and plantations, were placed there to take advantage of the river trade and transportation. Some of them, however, especially on the lower Mississippi, failed to take into consideration one very important item: the character of the Mississippi. Like no other American river, perhaps, it has always had a habit of eating its own shores and of engulfing its own bends, of destroying that which it had made, and of creating new shores, new bends, new islands, with the changing whims of each flood and freshet, each month and year.

This is what happened at Kaskaskia, Napoleon and Prentiss, to name three of the outstanding examples of towns which were totally destroyed by the Mississippi. Others—Arkansas City, Ste. Genevieve, Greenville, Vicksburg and Rosedale—were by-passed by the river, left miles inland, though they were once situated close to the Mississippi.

Alone and brave above the great river, Kaskaskia, Illinois, in 1700, was "an outpost of civilization and culture. In a wilderness peopled largely by unlettered savages, the civilization and religion and learning of the West found their foothold." Kaskaskia, like the still older Cahokia upstream, saw the coming and going of adventurers and explorers and the makers of history. It saw three flags wave over its hundreds of houses—the flag of France, in the days when the Illinois shore was French, saw the coming of the British flag, and saw it fall before George Rogers Clark and his American frontiersmen and soldiers who brought the new American flag to Illinois and left it planted there forever

But Kaskaskia did not stay forever. Year by year, when floods receded, the point of land on which the first capitol of Illinois stood had grown smaller. The legislature and seat of government were moved in 1818 to Vandalia, for everyone could see that the river was bound to devour Kaskaskia. In 1880–81, the Mississippi cut savagely across the neck of land and Kaskaskia became an island, remains of which still lie in the river, now close to the Missouri shore.

One by one the old houses slipped into the swirling brown water; fewer people remained to defy the river. In 1906 a single chimney stood on a bank above the water—and when that chimney fell down under the relentless river's rising current, that was the end of old Kaskaskia.

Down at the mouth of the Arkansas River, the town of Napoleon, Arkansas, was built. Men believed it would live up to its grand name, become as fine as New Orleans. Napoleon, however, became a rough, tough, rowdy town, instead of a dignified metropolis on two rivers. But in a few years it was plain to see what was going to happen. Napoleon suffered the fate of so many river towns, the fatal combination of war and the river.

The War between the States almost destroyed Napoleon by fire, and when the big flood of 1874 came along, after many floods had cut down on Napoleon's acreage no little bit already, the inhabitants finally gave up and moved south down the Mississippi. They built a new town which they called Arkansas City. They fondly hoped it would be let alone. This, of course, the river did not do. It has been all over the landscape down there, too. Right now, it has virtually deserted Arkansas City. With sandbars and islands grown fast to land in front of it, the town is now a considerable distance from navigable water. The river, however, completely destroyed Napoleon. There is nothing left. It is "swallowed up, vanished, gone to feed the fishes," as Sam Clemens remarked with genuine horror, for he had known Napoleon and its people when it was a living city.

Something like that happened just across the river, in Prentiss, Mississippi. On the navigation maps today, the spot is designated as Mile 575, and, in small print, *Prentiss Landing* In a way, those words are a grave-marker for another town which the river killed.

Once a lively place, rival of Napoleon, Prentiss had a race-track and the high life which goes with it. The town flourished for a while in the dangerous bottomlands opposite the mouth of the Arkansas River, until two Yankee gunboats came along during the War between the States. It happened that the old men and boys of Prentiss, either too old or too young to fight and resenting bitterly their inadequacy, saw the gunboats sliding downstream like big gray turtles and rashly fired their squirrel-rifles at them.

This was an invitation for some high, wide and handsome shelling from the gunboats. They shelled the woods where the misguided patriots were hidden, came back downstream and bombarded Prentiss itself for good measure, then put a party ashore to set fire to everything which would burn. That happened in 1863, and when the Yankees finished with Prentiss there wasn't much high life left in the old place. It was nearly a ghost town when the river turned to the attack.

Year after year the Mississippi, urged by the violent eddies of the outpouring Arkansas River, determinedly ate into the Prentiss banks, and every year, when the river was flooding, it piled about a foot of mud on top of the last silt laid down. The people went away and after a few years the entire town, what remained of it, was completely buried in the river's deposits.

In the spring of 1954, a couple of hunters broke through the tall dead weeds along the river shore, and to their amazement, they discovered a jutting, mud-caked chimney and side of a brick wall stuck into and parallel against the sheer bank of the river, where the water, methodically eating it away, uncovered what it had once buried. Men came with spades and dug around, here and there, to see what they could find. They located some corroded brass candlesticks, an old china teapot, a whiskey jug, some champagne bottles—odds and ends of the cast-offs of living—but they did not work very long, for the river was apparently determined to devour that shore, remains and all.

Far to the north of the three dead towns lies what is probably the youngest settlement on the Mississippi. Bemidji, Minnesota, about twenty miles from Lake Itasca, where the infant Mississippi starts forth on its long journey, was begun in 1894. It started on a false note, however, for settlers, discovering shining pebbles on the shores of Lake Bemidji, hastily concluded that they had found diamonds. A frenzy of land-buying immediately began, but lasted only until the "diamonds" were diagnosed as ordinary quartzite.

Several years later, the lumber companies came into the great forests around the area, and Bemidji grew into a real town which possessed fourteen sawmills, all running full speed to slice up great pines into boards. The town was named for Chief Bemidji, a Chippewa whose lands were nearby.

Many of the towns on the upper river developed from the lumbering industry which was opening land and rapidly cutting down the once almost impenetrable forests through which Pike and Schoolcraft had with difficulty struggled. In the lumber business was Grand Rapids, and so was Brainerd, as well as Little Falls.

St. Cloud, however, in addition to being a stone-quarrying center, was once an outfitting post for the fur trade. And it was the fur trade which poured down the Red River Trail and the Rum River to the posts at Anoka and Elk River—furs out of the north country, bound for the southern markets.

This same source of furs came into the town which was developing on the east side of St. Anthony's Falls, at the head of navigation At this spot St. Paul grew as a great fur center and point of river trade, while on the west bank of the Falls stood Colonel Snelling's water mills, one cutting lumber to build structures on the army reservation of Fort Snelling, the other grinding wheat into flour—wheat which the soldiers on the reservation grew during their long, leisurely summers, when Indian trouble was in abeyance.

The mills were the nucleus which became Minneapolis. Here at the head of navigation, 1,596 miles from the Gulf, the two cities which grew up simultaneously may have seemed to outsiders to be an integrated unit, but then and now they have always been distinctive cities. The land which Zebulon Pike bought for two hundred dollars' worth of trinkets from the Sioux became the site of the tremendous Twin-City area, dominating the high point of river traffic.

Lumbering and furs—these, part of the Twin Cities' growth, also influenced the towns which sprang up along the river below. Wacouta, at the head of Lake Pepin, once was a large town which was a center for lumbering, a river port of some size in the 1850's. Millions of logs were rafted to the bays around Wacouta, from up the St. Croix, to be sent southward. So many of the upper-river towns, now small and comparatively insignificant, were large and important until the pines were all cut, the beaver all but gone and the steamboats vanished.

A town which did not languish when furs and lumber waned is La Crosse, Wisconsin, down at the mouth of the Black River, a point at which millions of logs and rafts once came down to the larger stream. La Crosse, with its brewing and manufacturing businesses, continues to be spacious and prosperous as it carries on a large river trade today.

Sixty miles down the Mississippi is Prairie du Chien, which, contrary to most of the towns on the upper river, is one of the oldest on its entire reach. For a long time Prairie du Chien was a gathering place for Indian tribes, then it became a trading post, when Nicholas Perrot erected Fort St. Nicholas as early as 1685, two years before La Salle was murdered in Texas. Indians brought thousands of furs to the American Fur Company at Prairie du Chien, and trading boats coming up the river to buy them were laden with gaudy trinkets and more practical wares. Summer was a lively, bustling time in the old town. With the coming of winter and the freezing of the river, the Indians went home, the traders went south. Prairie du Chien, losing much of its color and activity, settled down to isolation and deep snow until the arbutus bloomed again, the ice went out, and Indian canoes and traders came back once more.

It was Julien Dubuque, a French Canadian who came to Prairie du Chien as a fur trader in 1785, who became a lead miner down the river in Iowa, in what was then Spanish territory. For lead, discovered by Renault's prospectors during the time of the Mississippi Bubble, was still one of the chief products which called people to that part of the Mississippi. Julien Dubuque's lead mine country became Dubuque, Iowa. This did not take place, however, until 1833, when Black Hawk and his chiefs signed a treaty with the settlers to make the area and its mines available to white men.

The stronghold of Black Hawk, Rock Island, lies a few miles south of Dubuque. Here Fort Armstrong was built on Campbell's Island, followed later by the great United States Arsenal and the city of Rock Island, with Moline and East Moline closely around it.

Davenport, Iowa, just across the river, forming the fourth of the Quad-Cities, was originally Colonel Davenport's trading post, part of the extensive American Fur Company. It was marked with the goings and comings of the French, Indians, traders and trappers. Not until 1856 did Davenport, Iowa, have railroad service from the East. When the first railroad bridge on the Mississippi spanned it in that year, not only that city but much of the West were suddenly connected with Chicago, the eastern states and the Atlantic Coast.

Fur posts and sawmill towns—the river was marked with many of them. Muscatine, Iowa, was one. When furs and lumber were about gone, the town in 1891 acquired a new business, derived from the depths of the river washing its shores. The once abundant fresh-water mussels, dredged out and cleaned of their meat, made the finest of pearl buttons. Over-pollution and over-harvesting, however, caused Mississippi clams to grow scarce. Muscatine today still manufactures a large percentage of the nation's pearl buttons made of clam shells brought by river boat up from the Ohio, the Cumberland and the Tennessee.

Below Muscatine is Fort Madison, attacked by Black Hawk's war band in the War of 1812, and below that is Keokuk, named for Chief Keokuk of the Sacs, who was the peace-maker during those late unpleasantries between Indians and whites. Opposite lies Nauvoo, old city of the Mormons and Icarians.

And there is Hannibal, Missouri, down a way. It was not an important town until it was put on the map by Samuel Clemens, who gave the place reality and life in the form of those two lovable little "river rats," Tom Sawyer and Huckleberry Finn. Their adventures, real or fancied, on, in, or beside the Mississippi personified life in the typical river town, as people liked to think of it. Perhaps no other two persons have so given meaning to life on the Mississippi as Tom and Huck. Throughout the world their names and that of their creator are synonymous with the Mississippi River.

Savanna, Sabula, Port Byron, LeClaire, Quincy, Canton, Graf-
ton, Elsah—they are all river towns, old in the ways of the river,
and part of its story. Below the mouth of the Illinois, there where
the high white cliffs make an undulating wall on the Illinois
shore, stands Alton, a town dominated by the river—by lock and
dam, by the big bridges, by the river cliffs and by the river itself,
which long ago sliced down through the bluffs and provided a site
for a city. Alton grinds up that limestone for cement, ships it
out, together with coal and glass bottles from one of the largest
bottle factories in the world.

And twenty-two miles south, by water, is St. Louis, at the spot
where, long ago, Frenchmen saw a city on the Indian mounds
and bluffs above the river. It was still French territory at a time
when the British were taking over the settlements on the eastern
shore, and selected because of this, as well as by the fact that
powerful Fort de Chartres, in Illinois, guarded it from below.

La Clede, a merchant up from New Orleans, stored his supplies of trade goods at the fort and sent his teen-age helper,
young Auguste Chouteau, to build a stockade and the beginning
of a town at the site which he had pointed out to him earlier.
It was youthful Chouteau's job to start a settlement before his
employer and friend, La Clede, came back. The young man was
capable and efficient. He had the seeds of St. Louis begun before
the handsome La Clede came by keelboat up the river.

St. Louis at once became a fur trading center, port for furs
brought by flatboat and piroque and canoe down from the north
country, handy to trade from the Missouri as well. St. Louis for
a long time was French—among the first families being the
Chouteaus—but when European politics bandied around this
city, together with the entire western shore of the Mississippi, it
happened that St. Louis, much against its will, came under the
Spanish flag.

The French inhabitants were angry and rebellious. They frequently gave Governor Ulloa and the Spanish military a bad
time of it. The times were uneasy for everyone. And when, after

the Louisiana Purchase, St. Louis and the west shore became, not French, not Spanish, but American, it was almost too much to bear. As the people reacted in New Orleans at that time, there was in St. Louis a period of mourning for a lost heritage, a lost honor, a lost flag

Out of furs and the river St. Louis grew. It became one of America's great river ports, a vital part of the character of the Mississippi. Dozens of steamboats tied up at the waterfront as long as the river was open. It was when a great many were tied close together that, on the dreadful night of May 17, 1849, a fire started on the wharves and spread to the steamboat *White Cloud.*

The wind rapidly carried the flames from one boat to another, until several were blazing furiously. They burned through their mooring hawsers and, shoved by wind and current, went bumping along the line of steamboats, setting fire to each, until most of the waterfront was blazing Twenty-nine steamboats perished in that holocaust which also burned many blocks of St. Louis.

A few years later, in the cold winter of 1856–57, many steamboats were caught in a huge ice gorge which, rearing twenty to thirty feet high, moved inexorably down on the ships and literally ground to pieces forty steamboats.

But still the steamboats came to St. Louis. They were part of its life and personality. Out of its shipyards, during the War between the States, emerged ironclads and gunboats, and out of those shipyards today come long, steel, highly efficient, powerful modern towboats and lesser craft. St. Louis is still a vital river port, doing big business on the waters.

Downstream stands Ste. Genevieve, Missouri, now four miles away from the river on which it once found much of its livelihood. After many floods, it was decided to move the old French town inland a distance to the hills, but soon after the move was laboriously accomplished, the river suddenly by-passed its old route, left a huge sandbar behind and surged along many miles from where it used to flow.

Cape Girardeau down the river, like Ste. Genevieve, began as a French trading center, dealing in furs and lead. In ancient times, the Gulf of Mexico lapped Cape Girardeau's rocky cliffs. Across the river is the spot where old Kaskaskia once stood, now vanished into oblivion and the river.

At the junction of the Ohio and the Mississippi stands Cairo. It was begun in 1818 by Kaskaskia men who saw in its strategic location the possibility of a valuable site for a city. Its two rivers drained half a continent and commanded all the life and commerce influenced by those lengthy streams.

But, in spite of golden promises and shining plans, the newly organized city remained a city on paper, and the real Cairo, planned to be built on a bed of silt laid down by high waters of two rivers, remained a mere woodyard at which steamboats paused for fuel.

At last, in 1837, Cairo awakened and started out to be a town. With two mighty rivers forever licking at her levees, Cairo could not help but remain painfully aware of them. The town has always had the difficult position, besides, of being located between two other opposing forces, of lying at the boundary between two kinds of people and, in the past, between two beliefs over which a war was fought. Cairo, as part of Illinois, is considered Northern, and during the War between the States was expected to fight for the Union. But just across the river lies Kentucky—the South.

Cairo people were more Southern in background, in sympathy, way of talk and leanings, than they were Northern, as they still are. Consequently, during the War between the States there were many internal troubles in Cairo, as the city was split in conviction. When General Grant stationed troops there and built Fort Defiance, and when Cairo became the assembly point for the Western Flotilla of gunboats, then her position, politically if not truly sympathetically, was settled.

Helena, Arkansas, has had her own troubles, with both a hungry river and a by-passing river. And below, on the Fourth Chickasaw Bluff on the east shore, stands Memphis. Because the bluffs are only forty feet above the normal height of the river, the city frequently has seen high water at the front door. The Spanish and French long ago had arguments over who should have the site of Memphis, while the Chickasaws, who had it first, were difficult to deal with. For a while, in retaliation, the Indians lurked on the bluffs and fired on keelboats and flatboats of the Spanish coming down from St. Louis, bound for New Orleans.

Around Memphis, for miles, in the rich bottomland laid down by the river, grow fields of cotton, which have made of Memphis a cotton metropolis. The big steamboats of the past which hauled the massive bales were loaded from water line to a point as high as possible, and boats were built larger and larger to haul even greater loads. The tremendous white cargo plucked from Mississippi bottomland fields traveled down the river to New Orleans and to the ports of the world. Today it goes by barge down that same stream.

Below are several towns which were deserted by the Mississippi. Greenville once was on the river, but now stands eastward on an ox-bow lake, Lake Ferguson, which is all that remains after the Mississippi produced a cut-off, while Vicksburg is another town which felt the keen tooth of Mississippi movement. High on its bluff, the once impregnable Gibraltar of the Mississippi faced the river and had little fear of floods. The Centennial Cut-off, however, in 1876, changed the course of the river so that it all but ignored the old city. Not until the Yazoo was diverted to flow past Vicksburg on the old Mississippi route was the place assured of a continuing river future.

On another bluff lies Natchez, one of the oldest cities on the ancient river, though some of its early streets, the unsavory region dominated by old Silver Street below the bluff, have been devoured by the river. The Natchez Indians, fierce sun-worshippers, lived at White Apple Village on the bluff. This was the residence of the Great Sun, an absolute monarch who was believed to have descended from the sun itself. A temple to that orb, built on a mound eight feet high, contained an altar on which lay a reed basket where reposed the bones of the former Great Sun.

With a well-run government, lands ancestrally theirs and a proud and ancient culture, the Natchez were understandably annoyed when the French demanded their lands simply because they fancied them. The French built Fort Rosalie on the bluff, to solidify their stand.

The Natchez, for strength, allied themselves with the Yazoos and the Choctaws, though they proudly looked down upon them as inferiors. A plan was agreed upon whereby the three nations should rise one day against the French and destroy them. The Choctaws were to attack New Orleans, which was but poorly defended and was having trouble, besides, with slave insurrections. The Natchez and Yazoos were to attack Fort Rosalie, near White Apple Village, at the same moment, and thus confuse the French utterly.

But the Natchez would bow to no man No "dirty, conniving, insolent" Choctaw could tell the Sun People what to do or when to do it. So the Natchez went ahead and attacked Fort Rosalie ahead of time.

Only one white man escaped from the carnage. Half-crazed from his experience, he crept through the forests and cane-brakes and somehow got to New Orleans in time to tell of the intended raid. The city was thrown into a panic, but had sufficient warning to be prepared for the Choctaws, who were beaten off. Finally, after a year of warring, the Natchez were subdued.

Those who were captured were ignominiously sold as slaves.

Necks in chains, proud heads unbent, bronze skins shining in the summer heat, the Natchez were marched down the river to New Orleans. Proudest of them all, his eagle's eyes fixed on some point so distant in the heavens that only one who has communed with his brother, the sun, could know where he looked, walked the last Great Sun of the Natchez people.

On the Istrouma Bluff, which is fifty feet above the level of the Mississippi, yet only fifty-one feet above sea-level, stands Baton Rouge, capital of Louisiana. It and St. Paul, Minnesota, are the only two capitals of river states which actually stand beside the Mississippi. The tall finger of the modern white structure of the capitol building is visible far up and down the river.

Baton Rouge was the boundary between Indian tribes, location of the Red Stick, a city which has known seven governments by white men. It was ruled by the French, the English, the Spanish, and was under West Floridian, Louisianian, Confederate and American governments. It is the farthest deep-water port on the Mississippi, with a thirty-five-foot channel maintained from here to the Gulf of Mexico, 230 miles away.

Between Baton Rouge and New Orleans, behind the levees, are the plantations. Many are very old, the great houses either fallen into ruins or carefully restored to their old beauty, or replaced by newer, more efficient homes of today's planters. The old houses and their ancient, moss-draped oaks, only their tops visible from the river, are remnants of that world of the river which developed in some sixty years of the previous century, and which found its downfall in the freeing of the slaves who worked the plantations.

These plantations were the domain of the steamboats, which hauled passengers and produce, mail and machinery, livestock and laborers—as well as yellow fever and cholera—from landing to landing and from town to town. On a route 120 miles long, steamboats customarily made 1,025 stops on a single trip.

This portion of the Mississippi today is a land of varied aspects.

They range from the old classic columns of a deserted plantation mansion, to the trim white buildings of the hospital at Carrville which treats Hansen's disease, or leprosy. There are huge sugar refineries and oil refineries, to whose docks come sea-going tankers and freighters, flying foreign flags.

At the southern terminus of the old steamboat route, 110 miles up from the Gulf of Mexico, is New Orleans. Perhaps the most vivid city on the river, it is still flavored with all the elements which went into its building. After Bienville's earliest city blew down in a hurricane at the moment when John Law's Mississippi Bubble was exploding in his face, New Orleans was rebuilt, not once but several times. Although, in the building, Bienville, Vaudreuil, Perrier and other governors of Louisiana attempted to make of New Orleans a French city in the New World, and although the Spanish attempted to make it Spanish during their regime, neither succeeded very well. They could not transplant France or Spain to America. They only managed to create a unique city which is itself, New Orleans.

It took a long time to accomplish it. The streets were unpaved for many years, and the French ladies and gentlemen were considerably irked by what the mud did to their fine clothes. Alligators still slithered into the roadways. The earth was too soggy for the dead to be buried in it. The Choctaws still came, stolid, dull, dirty, odorous, watchful, bringing bay leaves and *filé* powder to barter in the market.

But the city held. The river neither washed it away nor did the alligators, Indians and cypresses reclaim it. It was taken over by the Spanish, was repossessed by the French, was twice burned, was rebuilt; was fought over during the War of 1812. Then it became American, which was a shock to the delicate sensibilities of the elegant Creoles, who looked down with distaste upon Americans. But after Andrew Jackson won the Battle of New Orleans and saved the city from the British, the Creoles thought differently about Americans and fondly renamed their *Place d'Armes* Jackson Square to show their undying affection and gratitude.

Always, the city was part of the Mississippi, forever dominated by the river which flows in a mighty curve past the crooked streets. These were laid out at angles with the river, not according to the compass, all the way out to Lake Pontchartrain.

On the warm river wind, one may detect the smells which mean New Orleans today—the aromas of the French Market with its special kind of coffee and hot doughnuts dusted with powdered sugar . . . the smells of pompano and crabs and shrimps and oysters . . . of fennel and *filé* and bay . . . of banana boats and the rich fragrance of coffee up from South America . . . of ripe strawberries and ligustrum flowers, and oleander and frangipani and oranges . . . the incense of the Cathedral, the special smell of Spanish moss and palmetto leaves. In it and around it and all about, one senses the presence of John Law, who dreamed a city, and of Bienville, who built it, and of all those others who developed, year by year, the New Orleans of today.

These are most of the towns of the river. Each has its own character which has been bestowed by the river itself, on whose sufferance the town stays and prospers, or is eaten up, to vanish forever from the world of men and the Mississippi.

CHAPTER TWENTY-ONE

1957: *"I will plant companionship thick as trees
along all the rivers in America."*
WALT WHITMAN

To Tony, the new deckhand on the towboat *Zephyr Queen*,
everything was strange, everything had to be learned. It was like
being in a different world. In the beginning, especially that first
day, he was afraid he'd never make the grade. Still, decking
was a job, and a well-paying one. It came when he needed it,
between high school and college, or maybe the army. And if he
wanted to, the job could lead to a permanent career on the river.
The captains and pilots had started that way, and so had the
engineers in charge of all the machinery down in the engine-
room.

The boy had been born and had lived all his eighteen years

in the Cajun country of western Louisiana. Only a few miles west of his home stood the huge Cities Service Refinery, on the deep Calcasieu River, near Lake Charles, forty miles from Texas. His father was employed at the refinery and had taken him all through it. Tony had seen the big pipelines in which flowed the black crude oil, coming in from the wells and storage tanks in Texas and Oklahoma, had seen where men changed it, process by process—heating, distilling, cracking by means of a catalytic powder—in topping towers, hydroforming units, "cat" crackers —into something one paid thirty or more cents a gallon for at the filling station. Or, they made it into other things, all of which had their uses, things like asphalt and kerosene and Diesel oil, butane and propane, synthetic rubber and airplane gas.

While the three great towers of the "cat" crackers pounded the atmosphere with deep concussions of sound, three huge steel barges moored at the pumping dock sank slowly into the Calcasieu River. Their ten compartments were filling with gasoline which was piped in through mammoth black hoses. Here was the first step in transferring the finished product—gasoline— from the intricate processes of the refinery to the consumer and his motor car, by way of barges and the river. Tankermen from the *Zephyr Queen* and refinery men in steel hats were perpetually on guard.

"Oh, gasoline's safe enough, if you handle it right," the big mate assured Tony when the boy mentioned danger.

When at last the barges were filled with eight thousand tons of gasoline, they were inspected by men in steel hats and Louisiana leisure. They flashed sunlight from metal mirrors into the depths to determine exactly how deep the gasoline was, marked and sealed each hatch, and then it was time to go.

The mate was out on the foredeck of the *Zephyr Queen*. Captain Griscom was up in the pilothouse of the towboat, working his steering levers. The engineer and oiler were in the throbbing engineroom with the three big Diesel engines, jumping to answer the captain's bell signals, as he moved his levers, reversed his rudders, turned neatly in a half-circle in the broad river. Out there, pelicans were diving for fish in the sunset. The towboat came up behind one of the big barges. Each one was three hundred feet long, fifty feet wide and eleven feet deep. Nine feet of that depth was underwater.

Efficiently, as if he were moving a checker into a space on a board, he eased the big boat squarely in until it just touched the first barge, not jarring it a particle. The mate and two deckhands leaped to throw lines around timberheads and cavels, linking boat and barge tightly together. Heavy steel wire rope was laced back and forth. Hogchains and clamps were tightened. The electric capstan on the foredeck whirred as the line put around it was tightened; it narrowed, strained, groaned. Ratchets were pulled by men whose muscles stood out with the effort. Tony, working his first ratchet, suddenly realized that there was hard labor to be done on a towboat.

With the first barge made fast against the towing knees at the bow of the boat, the growing tow moved in to connect with the second, and then with the third. In a little while, the three barges and boat were fastened tightly in one unit, stretched out more than a thousand feet, as long as an ocean liner. The whistle tooted three times, was answered by a blast from a seagoing tanker which had just moved up to the docks, and the *Zephyr Queen* swung her tow out into midstream and turned to the south.

Soon she entered the Gulf Intracoastal Waterway which connects New Orleans with Texas, passed through the Calcasieu Locks which keep salt water out of the rice fields, and was on her way steadily, eastward through the darkness, bound for the Mississippi River.

Next day the tow passed miles of sea-level marshes, land stretching to the Gulf of Mexico which glittered on the horizon in the morning sun. The boy's uncle had made a small fortune from muskrat pelts trapped in those marshes. He had another uncle who was foreman at the salt mine at Weeks Island. Other kin lived on the big rice plantations; some worked on the oil rigs standing out in the Gulf.

It was like surveying his past, going through the Waterway, and then into a wilder landscape where the cypress swamps of the Barataria country—Tony's grandparents came from there—reached to within a few yards of the boat. Passing the *Zephyr Queen* day and night were hurrying tugboats and many towboats, some hauling empty barges to the refineries, others returning, heavily loaded. The Waterway was like a busy highway.

When at last the *Zephyr Queen* and her eight thousand tons of gasoline were maneuvered through the Harvey Locks, opposite New Orleans, and came out into the broad, coffee-and-cream colored waters of the Mississippi, Captain Griscom sighed with relief. It was six o'clock in the morning. At five miles an hour, the towboat had traversed 255 miles of Waterway.

Tony was mopping the floor of the pilothouse, his regular morning duty, first thing.

"I'm always glad to get out of that 'ditch,' " said the captain, leaning back in his swivel chair, his feet cocked on the control panel so Tony could mop under them. Bill, another deckhand, was already at work, washing windows. "It's narrow and those blamed cypresses are too close for comfort. Thank goodness we're out with no trouble, and we've got about fifty feet of water under us. It's a pretty day, and I don't feel mad at anybody!"

Tony grinned up from his mopping. "You think it'll be as warm as this up where we're going?" he asked. He was in his shirt sleeves and was perspiring with his exertions in the March warmth of Louisiana.

"Warm—up in Minnesota—in March? Ha!" snorted Captain Griscom. "Don't make me laugh! Why, boy, we're likely to find snow four feet deep, and have to break our way through the ice to get to the pumping dock! It's early to go up there, but it's been a hard winter and they need the gasoline badly, I hear.

The river's open: the locks are operating, and I guess we'll make it."

"I've never seen snow," said Tony quietly, pausing to look out at a freighter flying the Norwegian flag, which was steaming past.

Steadily, still at five miles an hour, the *Zephyr Queen* traveled the bends of a rising Mississippi. In the abyss of darkness which closed down every night, Captain Griscom on the six-to-midnight shift, and Captain Henry on the late watch till dawn, serenely navigated by means of the big, powerful, blue-white arc lights. They searched out the bends and the shore blinkers, hunting out the buoys, staying always with the conical red buoys on the right and the black and white can buoys on the left.

The radar screen, endlessly moving its changing pattern of shore and river, like some surrealistic television, showed everything solid on the river or beside it. The short-wave radio phone was on. The captain talked to the captains of other boats miles up ahead, determining on which side each wished to pass and exchanging news, gossip and friendliness across the darkness.

To Tony, it looked like an easy job, just sitting comfortably in the pilothouse for six hours at a stretch, then sleeping or reading for a like amount of time, ready to go on duty for another six hours, with wonderful meals regularly spaced, coffee at intervals and snacks on tap at all times. He mentioned this to Captain Griscom one day.

"Look, Tony, you never really relax on the Mississippi! It may not look like it to you, but I'm like a cat on a hot stove, waiting for the river to pull one of its tricks—"

And so one fine spring day the river pulled its trick—or, rather, the *Zephyr Queen* did, which amounted to the same thing. Trouble!

Quite suddenly and without any warning, the steering gear went dead. The horizontal levers might have been made of soft rubber, for all the good they did. The captain had been heading straight across the river on a crossing, to go around Belle Island Corner Light, so the *Zephyr Queen*, rather inconveniently, was pointed straight at a shore when it happened.

"Brace yourself, kid," said Captain Griscom quietly to Tony, hastily ringing the engineroom to shut off the engines. But even at five miles an hour and with the three engines dead, the forward momentum of eight thousand tons of cargo carried the tow inexorably head-on into the shore.

The thirty-foot sand embankment crested with forest collapsed hugely on top of the first barge as it struck. Two medium-sized cottonwoods and a deciduous holly tree in full bloom came down, along with various smaller debris from the woods. The two in the pilothouse simply watched, helpless to do anything.

The barge finally stopped pushing and drifted off. Crosswise in the river, the *Zephyr Queen* floated helplessly downstream toward the nearest sandbar. Just in time, the engineers had the rudders repaired, and the captain, vastly relieved, got squared away, with the barges moving properly upstream again. Atop the first barge was a mountain of sand and earth.

Tony heaved a sigh. He picked up the Captain's empty coffee cup and the scrub bucket and started for the stairs.

"I reckon there's about eight or nine tons of dirt down there," he said in parting, "and I reckon I'd better get on to the business end of a shovel and start shoveling. . . ."

It took Bill and Tony until noon to get about half of the stuff off. Joe and Russell finished the job that afternoon. But for days there was a scattering of little white holly flowers patterned like confetti on the dark red-brown floor of the barge.

Two more days, placid, uneventful, steady and slow. The wind was cooler now, not so springlike. Heavy fogs rose after midnight and turned the world of the river into a nothingness of white. Without radar, the captains would have had to tie up. Other tows were going along, a great many of them, night and day, loaded with gasoline, coal and fuel oil, heading north with the

Zephyr Queen. They made a splendid parade, going to the rescue of the freezing North—the huge *Aetna-Louisville,* the *Mark Twain,* the *Coral Sea,* the *Guadalcanal,* the *Harriet M.,* the *Celeste,* the *Illini,* the *St. Louis Zephyr* and the *LaCrosse Socony,* with always another around the next bend.

Unknown to anyone, a certain bluff shoal had moved a few yards from its old site. Unmarked and invisible, the masses of heavy sand enveloped the iron-hard bulk of an old dead tree, pointing like a huge spear downstream. . . .

Captain Henry, on the early watch, had just turned in his chair to adjust the short-wave when the impact sent him headlong into the corner. When he regained consciousness a moment later, the boat had stopped, with the engines laboring and grinding. Suddenly, as the captain got to his feet and looked hastily out, blinking, it seemed to him that the whole Mississippi River, in the dawn light, was red, bright strawberry red. Red! His wits clear instantly. *Red!* That meant gasoline—gasoline—spreading all over the river. A barge was snagged, was leaking gasoline, flooding the river with red gas . . . and that port engine shooting sparks up the chimney like a Roman candle!

Fast as he could, Captain Henry rang the engine room to shut off the engines, all of them. One spark on that insidious scarlet tide . . . one spark . . . The mate raced to turn off the galley stove. No man lit a cigarette. Everyone, in silence—some still in their pajamas, the cook in her hair-curlers and bathrobe—tensely came out on the lower deck and, quietly and hardly breathing, watched 2,400 barrels of gasoline flood past them down the placid, dawn-lit Mississippi River.

The *Zephyr Queen* finally got off the sandbar. However, after the gasoline had been let out from one entire compartment of the damaged barge, it had immediately filled with water, which, being heavier than gasoline, made that barge sink lower in front that it should. The air hose was run in and compressed air pumped in to replace some of the water. The barge, thus light-

MISSISSIPPI CALLING

237

ened, rose to the proper level of the tow. Almost as if nothing had happened—as if the leading barge did not have a great hole in its bow—the *Zephyr Queen* continued up the Mississippi.

Past the miracle of Memphis rising from the river shore . . . under the bridge, northward, hour after hour, past the great spreading mouth of the Ohio, with the triangle of Cairo dividing the two streams. At Cape Girardeau, the injured barge was left off at the shipyard, to be pumped out and gas-freed at great expense. Then the great hole would be repaired.

"Probably cost the Company $15,000 or so; maybe more," commented Captain Griscom glumly. "Can't say they'll like it."

Gone was the pleasant springtime warmth of the South. There was a day of chill, gray rain when the towboat tied up at her home dock below St. Louis for a refueling. Tony thought he had never been so cold in his life. He was kept too busy, however, to complain. He knew what to do now, and did it fairly well. Tie off the barges at a pile cluster upstream, come back to the fueling dock. Hoses to the Diesel tanks in the engine-room; hoses to the water tanks. Joe, one of the deckhands, appears in his good clothes, suitcase in hand, and goes ashore for his twenty days off at home, and Jeff, his replacement, comes on. Mail is brought aboard. The captain goes up the hill to telephone the Home Office and get his orders.

North again . . . past the noise of the shipyard, past the lights of St. Louis, under the bridges, into Lock Number 27 at Chain of Rocks, 1,200 feet long, . . . past the mouth of the muddy Missouri . . . and Alton Lock, Number 26, where the big dam roared white water and gulls circled.

Number 26 was a six-hundred-foot lock, which meant that the tow had to be taken apart, the barges tied side by side to fit into the 110-foot width. Then they went through, were lifted on the rising water to a higher level, the green light flashed, the whistle blew, and the gates at the upper end opened to let boat and barges out. There they had to be reassembled, retied —and this had to be done over at every one of the locks ahead, all twenty-five, with the exception of Number 19, newly built and 1,200 feet long.

"You be sure that line's tight, and I mean tight!" warned the mate, watching Tony pull on his ratchet until his biceps stood out. "No, tighter than that. Do I have to tell you every time? These two barges got to be so close and snug you couldn't hardly slip a dime between them. I don't aim to have any barges of mine break away, ever!"

"Don't see how they could," grumbled Tony, straining at the ratchet.

"They can and they do," said the mate sternly. "You tie a barge wrong, it snaps those lashings like they were string Once it gets loose, a barge goes crazy, and you do, too, trying to catch it. There was a full gasoline barge I heard about once. It started off downstream like a freight train, wrapped itself around a bridge abutment and blew up. Company don't hold with stuff like that! Mate they had on relief once when I was home, he let a barge get away, and they had one awful time even finding it. It was night, and they lost track of it, and that barge slipped into a side bayou and kept going, while the *Zephyr Queen* ran miles down the river, hunting. Finally got word from a helicopter pilot that he'd sighted a barge down a little back-water bayou, and was it ours? No, you make sure those lashings are tight, boy!"

Spring was decidedly seeping out of the landscape. By the time the tow reached Rock Island and Lock and Dam Number 15, the country looked wintery. At Lock Number 10, Guttenberg, Iowa, it was starting to rain, mixed with snow. If that was snow, Tony decided, he didn't care for it.

That night Captain Griscom navigated blind. The snow was coming down in earnest now, sweeping in from the northwest, and it was as dense as fog. Even the powerful arc lights could not slice through that smother. But the radar was working. With his face down in the radar hood, his hands on the steering lever, Captain Griscom was running that explosive tow straight up the winding channel of the upper Mississippi River, through the confusing jumble of islands in the Winneshiek Marshes, heading toward Lake Pepin.

A jolt wakened Tony and nearly tumbled him on the floor. The engines were groaning and grinding, the boat quivering. He piled out of his bunk and pried open a slat in the blinds, to look out, but all he could see was that sickening white smother of snow, which had even whitened the barges.

"We're aground," mumbled Bill from his bunk. "Nothing to worry about. We'll get off. Always do."

Tony was not so sure. The boat was making an awful to-do, and he could feel how Captain Henry, up there in the dark, was feeling for the channel, sort of inching fan-wise until the rudders and propellers caught hold again in deep water. That was the moment when Tony saw the dark shape drifting past his window.

"Bill!" he yelped. "A barge! There's a barge broke loose!"

That brought Bill out on the deck. So did the four long blasts on the whistle, the disaster signal. Everyone threw on his clothes, fast, and hurried out on the slippery barges. The first one, in striking the sandbar, had indeed broken loose. Sometimes the best-tied lines break under strain. Ratchets and wire rope had flown violently into the river.

"Get your lines ready," ordered the mate, who was in his pajamas and life jacket. "Captain's going to circle and we got to chase that barge. When we get in close, he'll cut the engines and let us sort of ease up to it. You try to loop a timberhead or cavel, or anything you can drop a line over. Take it easy, now. Hey, you, Jeff, get your life jacket on. You know it's against regulations to work out here without it!"

The captain brought the boat and remaining barge around and followed gently behind the fleeing member. Quietly he coasted up to it, and the men with their heavy manila lines threw their loops, but they fell short. Dragged up from the water, they were twice as heavy as before. Again the men swung —and again they missed.

Next time Jeff caught a timberhead and pulled in. Bill got a cleat—and by that time they had the barge captured. Firmly and persuasively, they worked the runaway around the side of the tow and brought it to its front position again, without once letting it loose. Again it was tied with more wires and manila lines and hogchains and clamps, while the snow came down silently like great feathers, through which the arc lights were a blue-white blur edged with purple.

The barges were slippery with ice and snow the next morning when Tony and Bill went out to bring in the running lights, but the snow had stopped falling.

Captain Griscom was worrying about the cold weather.

"Weather report says it's going to get down to fifteen degrees by tonight, and if that Lake Pepin starts to freeze up, we'll be stuck at St. Paul till it thaws, *if* we get so far. I sure don't like the look of it. This trip has had *everything*, so far, but a good hard freeze. I never saw the like!"

They got through angry Lake Pepin without any trouble. Once she had escaped from its dangerous width and wind and waves, the *Zephyr Queen* moved into a narrowing Mississippi. Ice was forming in bays and shallows, but boats were keeping the channel open. Snow lay everywhere on shore. It looked like Christmas cards, especially where there were evergreen trees on the hills and little red houses and barns, but Tony, shivering, decided he preferred the South to this.

Redwing; Diamond Bluff; Lock Number 2 at Hastings. And ahead stood the tall smokestacks of St. Paul and Minneapolis, the big, waiting, almost empty oil tanks, the depleted coal dumps. The *Mama Lere* and the *Memphis Zephyr* were unloading coal when the *Zephyr Queen* shoved up to the pumping dock at eleven o'clock on a cold March night. Old snow drifts lay all about. St. Paul and Minneapolis looked like the middle of winter.

Snowflakes were beginning to come down again when Captain Griscom, with some difficulty, maneuvered the boat and barges closer to the dock, calling orders through the bullhorn, slanting his arc lights down to show the deckhands where the dock was. Tony was doing it all wrong, and the mate was getting out of patience. Bill slipped and nearly went overboard, and that scared the mate so that he was angrier than ever. Tony cut his wrist on the wire rope. At that interesting moment the bullhorn conked out and the arc lights failed. The captain yanked open a window and yelled through the megaphone into the snow, but his voice didn't carry well in the thick atmosphere.

He fingered the levers, backing, advancing, circling, breaking the ice so that the barges could get into the pumping dock. It was exhausting, nerve-wracking work, but by midnight they were in, barges tied off, and the Zephyr Queen moored some distance away for safety.

Thankfully, Bill and Tony went off watch, had some cherry pie and a cheese sandwich and milk, shucked their wet clothes and went to bed. They left the rest of the business to Jeff and Russell, who had had to pile out of warm bunks and plunge into the cold and snow, to supervise the pumping out of fuel brought over 1,800 miles of hazards, from Louisiana to Minnesota. Great black hoses were let down and connected with the manifolds. Pumping out began. Snow was flittering like butterflies in the lights of the dock, and the water was black and restless and menacing, with dirty-looking ice floes floating in it.

The Zephyr Queen had arrived. Her mission was completed. Yet hers was just a routine trip. It was no great adventure, except perhaps for the new boy, Tony, but she and her crew had been part of the great push north, to bring fuel to emptying tanks. They had been an integral part of today's story of the Mississippi. Tony sensed this importance. And he also no longer felt an alien on the river. He, like the *Zephyr Queen*, belonged.

The *Zephyr Queen* and her journey from the far south to the north represents today on the river. Typical of boats, cargoes, men and missions of the present River Era, she carries the story of the Mississippi up to the present. What will come tomorrow and the days after tomorrow, no one can say, but without much doubt the Mississippi will still be there, still will influence the men whose lives are ensnared along its massive, magnificent, unforgettable length.

CHAPTER TWENTY-TWO

"The river of God is full of water."
BOOK OF PSALMS

THE channel of the Mississippi is a river within a river. Invisible on the surface, the channel is there, weaving its own unpredictable way back and forth across the Mississippi, following a deeper cut on the irregular bottom than does the rest of the water.

The endless problem of the navigator is to determine where that channel is today, this hour, this minute; where, exactly, it runs close to the bank, where it follows the middle, where it cuts over to the other side by an invisible but vital crossing. It may change sides half a dozen times in as many miles and must be followed carefully, except during high water, when most of the river is navigable.

Down on the murky bottom of the Mississippi lie deep canyons and high hillocks. These and other obstructions very likely determine where this river-within-a-river runs, but why it changes so frequently and so unpredictably is something which no man, perhaps, will ever quite understand.

Yet men know that, usually, the channel cuts close to the outer curve of a loop or bend, because silt drops near the inner bend, to make the water shallower. They know, also, that the channel is something so easily misplaced, even today, when they follow between the faithful red and black buoys, that without constant attention to the look of the river, the inscrutable rightness of the channel, they may find their boats foundering on a shoal, ramming a sunken barge, or nosing up into the trees of an island or towhead.

The heights and depths of the river bottom are caused by natural obstructions. These may be rocks and ridges, massive sand bars and gravel bars, as well as heavy, octopus-armed snags which will never float again, wrecked steamboats and river equipment and other sizeable impedimenta which have found their last resting place in the river.

Around these lumps and hummocks and cunningly concealed masses, in the deep pits and valleys, the swift current of the river shoves and swirls and seldom runs straight.

On the surface, these swirls may show as strange, polished, boiling spots, surrounded with churning ripplets catching the sun, or by crazy, erratic leapings and twirlings of the agitated water. Sometimes an eddy that begins to boil around an obstruction grows wilder and broader and stronger, churning around and around, carrying drift and small boats if it catches them. It chews out the nearest bank in a circular sort of hollow. The earth, crumbling away under its onslaught, dumps trees and fishing shacks overboard.

There have been whirlpools in the Mississippi which were more than three hundred feet broad, cupped twenty to thirty feet deep, angrily circling and throwing the fright of their lives into rivermen, who had difficulty in getting away from the insidious pull of that boiling demon of an eddy.

And then the peaceful-seeming river may turn glassy-smooth on a calm day. It may be gray as ice when there is weather brewing and the wind has not raised; or slashed into angry waves, frothing with high-flung foam when the wind hits. Flying sand and rain obscure the shores so that the river looks like a stormy ocean. It can smooth itself just as quickly after a squall.

It may be submerged in fog which envelops everything with damp particles of mist so dense that ducks sit on the water and do not attempt to fly, herons with difficulty spy their prey, and boats proceed cautiously, if at all. The fog is silent and insidious, blowing, swirling, growing more dense, then breaking like magic and dispersing as clouds in a sunny sky.

And the river may look strangely opaque, a curious pale green, and smell of the sea, or it may look like liquid amber, or red as paint, or clear as air, or earth-gray and thick with mud boils; or it may look like coffee-and-cream, and smell of willows. From one end to the other, that willow perfume, compounded of green leaves on the trees and dead leaves on shore, is part of the Mississippi. It is as much an ingredient of the river as its sandbars and its variable current. It is as much a quality inherent to the Mississippi as the great blue herons which seem to have taken over the fishing franchise on every bar and point and shore, or the black cormorants sitting like grotesque candles on the free-form candelabra of snags and dikes.

From hour to hour, the river changes. The water at sunset is full of reflected gilt and apricot and ultramarine, sliding in waves that are steel-gray between the color, or silver and black, as the light dims. It picks up the starshine when night is dark upon the water. Stars with the brilliance of Sirius or Vega or Arcturus, or the glowing planets Venus and Jupiter, actually make paths of shimmering light across the moving, sibilant night waters of the Mississippi, when the smell is of honeysuckle, or basswood bloom, or of wood smoke from a fisherman's fire.

Moonlight changes the water to pale silver, against which the trees are black and distinct. River lights, set to mark each mile and bend and point, twinkle like the fireflies flittering with their over-sized sparks in the bottomlands. Small fish leap out in troops, like flying fish, flash white in the searchlight of a boat and drop back again. Frogs' eyes on the shore-edge catch the glare and glint green. The sky is darker silver, oxidized by night, specked with stars. Low-moving fog, which rises after midnight, wavers above the mystic, living waters like smoke from a cauldron, then climbs and glimmers and finally vanishes as the orange light of dawn grows against the rim of black, dew-wet trees in the east.

Dragonflies waken in the willows, and the shores come alive with bird song. Light blossoms on the waters. The unutterably fresh, damp scent of the river, the wet-sand smell, the dry-sand smell, the mud smell, the smell of swamps and cypresses, of sycamores and sedges, of lotus blossoms and cattail pollen, the dawn aroma itself, are all there, integrated in the morning— along with that ever-present willow perfume.

Daybreak, and a new day on the river has begun. It will be different from all others in the way in which the Mississippi shifts another sandbar a little way downstream, or gnaws madly with slashing teeth into a caving bank and topples live trees into the water. It will toss chunks of brown foam like floating bread upon the current, to show that another bank has gone into the maw of the Mississippi, to be built on somewhere else, some other time.

The river will be different, too, especially if there has been a rain upstream. It will send old black driftwood wallowing every which way, big as telephone poles and deadly to boat propellers. Perhaps the driftwood may be small enough for terns and dragonflies to hitch a ride—plunging and tugging and lolloping, or sliding easily downstream, always downstream, goal of all Mississippi driftwood.

Or the day may be gray, with rain vanishing in a gray river, a dim world of moisture, a world of water. The night of rain may be an abyss of blackness, without form or substance, only wetness. There may be snow sifting down in a white smother which vanishes in the brown waters, and there may be floating masses of ice, drifting swiftly on the current from far northward, when the river is breaking up in early spring. The white, patterned, silent bulk of the frozen Mississippi is shattered by the Coast Guard's ice-breaker boats, which shove through, grinding and struggling, to clear a way for the cargo vessels, laden with vital oil or coal, bound for ports on the Illinois.

The ever-moving Mississippi, even under the ice, can never let itself alone. For eons it has eaten into its own sandstone cliffs and into glacial sand deposits; it has busily carried the sand grains downstream to some other place. It has put a sandbar of some size at the mouth of all its larger tributaries . . . in the mouth of the Wisconsin, made of that river's own sandstone cliffs and the grinding of water through the Dells of the Wisconsin. It put an island in the mouth of the Illinois and covered it with willows and soft maples. It has put sandbars at the exit of the Missouri, and at the mouth of the rampaging Arkansas it has slammed a huge, ever-changing, hill-high mass of sand, with sheer sides and hideous lances of embedded stumps and trees thrusting out of it.

"That's a whole lot of water," the visitor says to the native at Hannibal or Rock Island or St. Louis or Memphis, watching the Mississippi go past, as if late for an appointment with destiny.

"Yeah, sure is," says the native reflectively and affectionately. "And you're only seeing the top of it!"

This is the Mississippi, still huge and wonderful and uncontrollable. It is that little ice-cold stream tumbling over rocks out of Lake Itasca, up in northern Minnesota; that river which runs red past the iron mines, and has been lightly harnessed by twenty-six dams; that same river which is added to mightily by the influx of the Missouri pouring mud out of the paint country of the West, all the way from the mountains of Montana, and by the Ohio which drains the country to New York State and Pennsylvania. It is the same magnificent, unpredictable, monstrous, magical, mysterious, terrible, potent body of water which carried glacier meltings to the Gulf, far back when the first men knew it, when they hunted mammoths beside the Mississippi . . . and back . . . and back . . . longer than any man can ever know. And it is the same dauntless river which flows confidently on and on into the future.

*   *   *

INDEX

VIRGINIA S. EIFERT

of Springfield, Illinois, is the author of Dodd, Mead's "Young Lincoln" trilogy. *The Buffalo Trace,* first of the three, tells of Abraham Lincoln's parents and grandparents. It received the *New York Herald Tribune's* Spring Book Festival Award in the oldest group and the Thomas Alva Edison Foundation's Award for the "Youth Book Best Portraying America's Past." It was dramatized on NBC's *Carnival of Books.*

Out of the Wilderness, second in the trilogy, takes Lincoln through childhood to young manhood, while *Three Rivers South* depicts Abraham Lincoln's flatboat trip down the Mississippi to New Orleans in 1831.

Out of the latter grew the idea for *Mississippi Calling,* which is really a "biography" of this fascinating, magnificent, challenging river.

To gain firsthand knowledge of the Mississippi, the author traveled more than 5,550 river miles as a guest aboard the two Diesel towboats, the *St. Louis Zephyr* and the *Cape Zephyr.*

At the leisurely pace of a towboat pushing its heavy barges of gasoline at five miles an hour, Mrs. Eifert studied the ever-changing moods of the great river. Above the head of navigation, at St. Paul–Minneapolis, she went by car and on foot to the source of the Mississippi at Lake Itasca, and thus became acquainted with almost every mile of that magnificent and complex stream.

CPSIA information can be obtained
at www.ICGtesting.com
Printed in the USA
LVHW081254210721
693300LV00002B/33